THE BEST GUITAR COLLECTI
OF ALL TIME

JUNE 2004

CW00428654

To/ Nick

Enjoy!!!!

Lots of Love

Mum xx

HAL LEONARD EUROPE
Distributed by Music Sales

Exclusive Distributors:

Music Sales Limited
8/9 Frith Street, London W1D 3JB,
England.

Music Sales Pty Limited
120 Rothschild Avenue, Rosebery,
NSW 2018, Australia.

Order No. HLE90001520
ISBN 0-7119-8732-7
This book © Copyright 2002 by
Hal Leonard Europe.

Cover photograph courtesy of Redferns.
Printed in the USA.

Your Guarantee of Quality
As publishers, we strive to produce every
book to the highest commercial standards.

The book has been carefully designed to
minimise awkward page turns and to make
playing from it a real pleasure.

Throughout, the printing and binding have
been planned to ensure a sturdy, attractive
publication which should give years of enjoyment.
If your copy fails to meet our high standards,
please inform us and we will gladly replace it.

Music Sales' complete catalogue describes
thousands of titles and is available in full colour
sections by subject, direct from Music Sales Limited.
Please state your areas of interest and send a
cheque/postal order for £1.50 for postage to:
Music Sales Limited, Newmarket Road,
Bury St. Edmunds, Suffolk IP33 3YB, England.

www.musicsales.com

STRUM AND PICK PATTERNS

This chart contains the suggested strum and pick patterns that are referred to by number at the beginning
of each song in this book. The symbols ⊓ and ∨ in the strum patterns refer to down and up strokes, respectively.
The letters in the pick patterns indicate which right-hand fingers plays which strings.

p = **thumb**
i = **index finger**
m = **middle finger**
a = **ring finger**

For example; Pick Pattern 2
is played: thumb - index - middle - ring

Strum Patterns   ## Pick Patterns

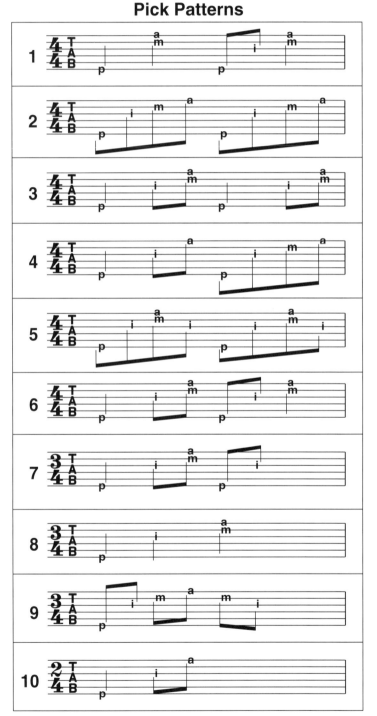

You can use the 3/4 Strum or Pick Patterns in songs written in compound meter (6/8, 9/8, 12/8, etc.).
For example, you can accompany a song in 6/8 by playing the 3/4 pattern twice in each measure.
The 4/4 Strum and Pick Patterns can be used for songs written in cut time (¢) by doubling the note
time values in the patterns. Each pattern would therefore last two measures in cut time.

All for Love

from Walt Disney Pictures' *The Three Musketeers*

Words and Music by Bryan Adams, Robert John "Mutt" Lange and Michael Kamen

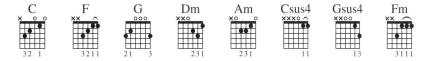

Strum Pattern: 3
Pick Pattern: 4

Moderately

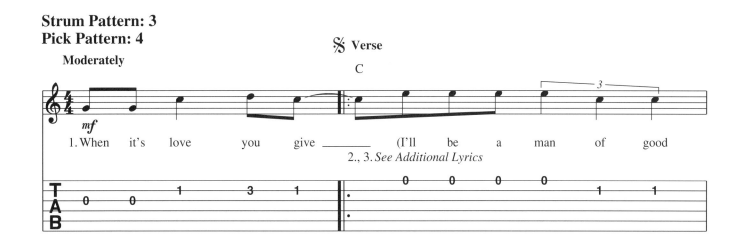

1. When it's love you give _____ (I'll be a man of good

2., 3. See Additional Lyrics

faith.) then in love you'll live. _____ (I'll make a stand. I won't break.)

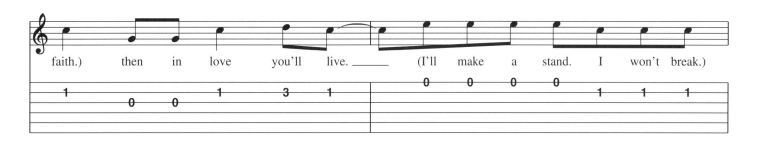

I'll be the rock you can build on,

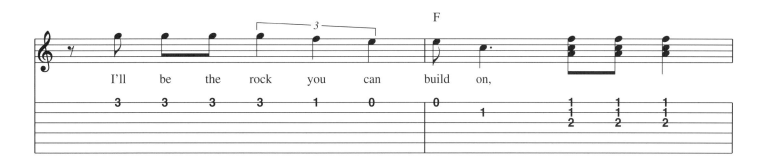

be there when you're old, to have and to hold. 2. When there's love in - side _____

Chorus

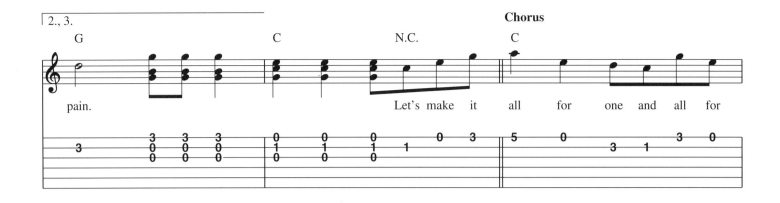

pain.   Let's make it all for one and all for

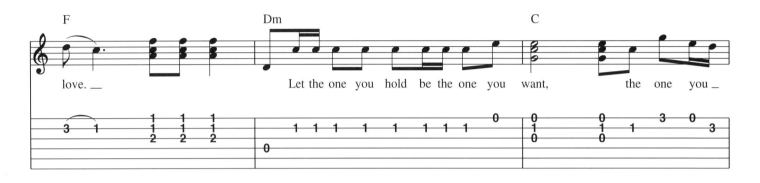

love. _   Let the one you hold be the one you want, the one you _

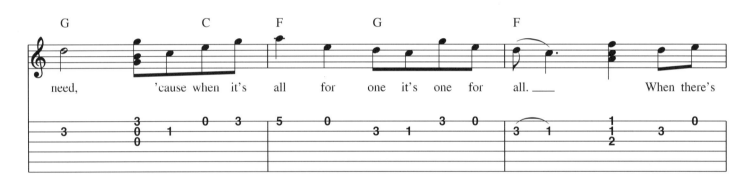

need,   'cause when it's all for one it's one for all. ___ When there's

some - one that should know then just let your feel - ings show and make it

To Coda ⊕   *D.S. al Coda*

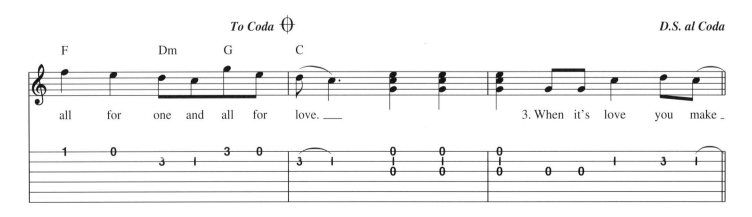

all for one and all for love. _   3. When it's love you make _

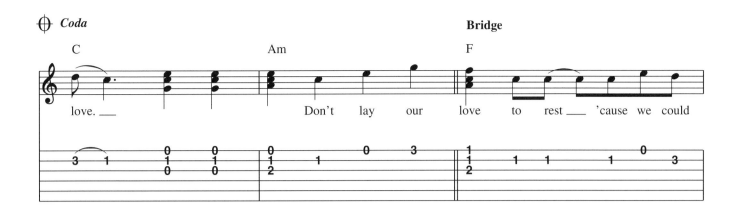

Coda

love. ___ Don't lay our love to rest ___ 'cause we could

Bridge

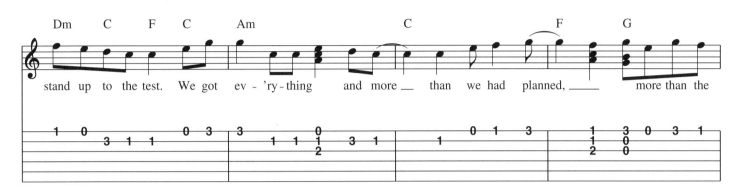

stand up to the test. We got ev - 'ry - thing and more ___ than we had planned, ___ more than the

riv - ers that run ___ the land. _____ We've got it all _____ in our hands.

Interlude

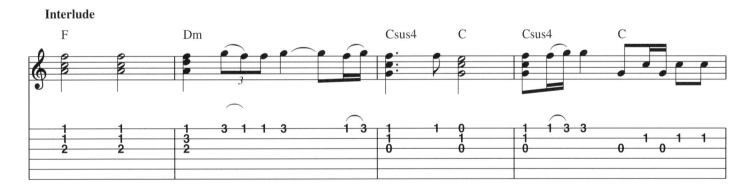

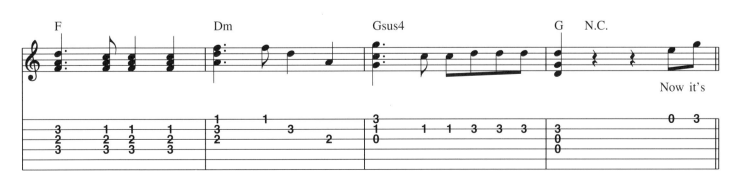

Now it's

Chorus

Additional Lyrics

2. When there's love inside (I swear I'll always be strong.)
   Then there's a reason why. (I'll prove to you we belong.)
   I'll be the wall that protects you from the wind and the rain,
   From the hurt and the pain.

3. When it's love you make (I'll be the fire in your night.)
   Then it's love you take. (I will defend, I will fight.)
   I'll be there when you need me.
   When honor's at stake, this vow I will make:
   That it's...

All the Things You Are

Lyrics by Oscar Hammerstein II
Music by Jerome Kern

Strum Pattern: 3
Pick Pattern: 5

Verse
Moderately

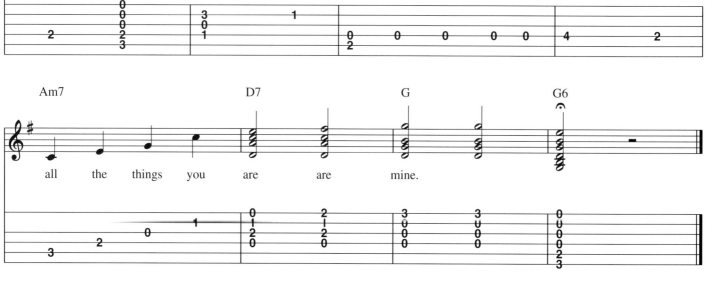

Blackbird

Words and Music by John Lennon and Paul McCartney

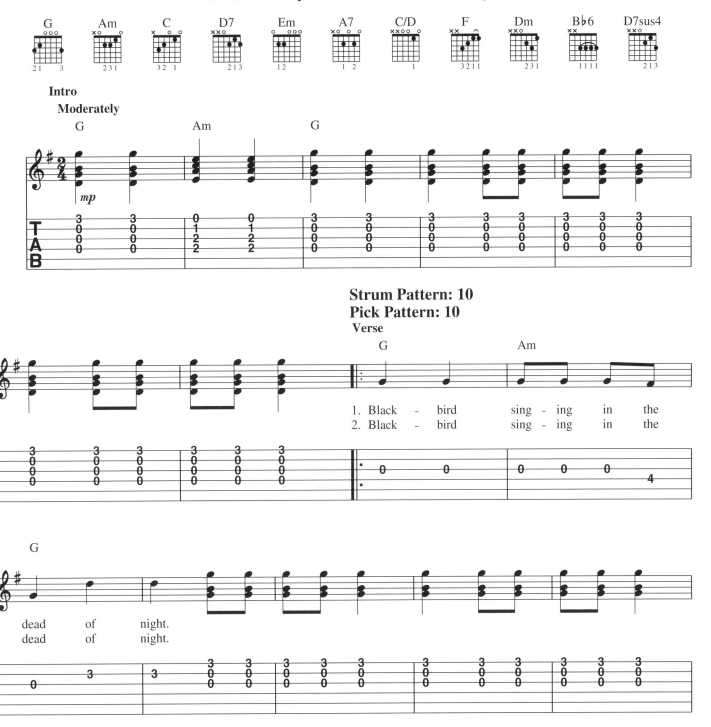

Strum Pattern: 10
Pick Pattern: 10

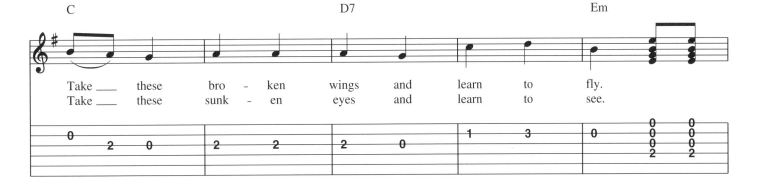

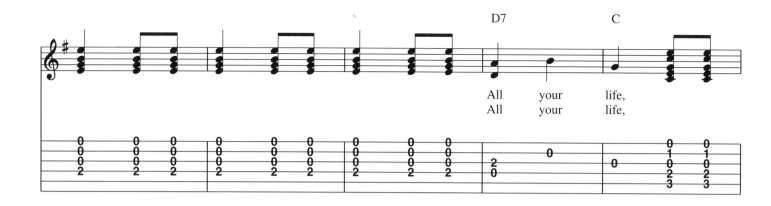

D7   C

All your life,
All your life,

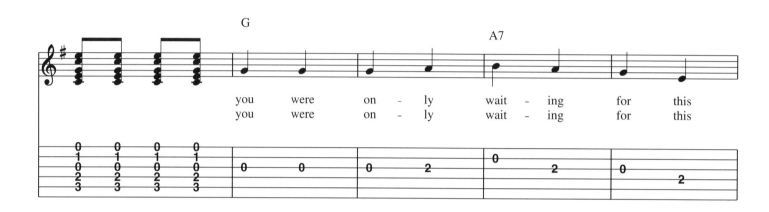

G   A7

you were on – ly wait – ing for this
you were on – ly wait – ing for this

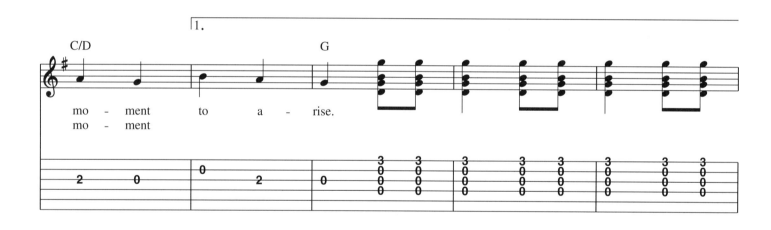

1.

C/D   G

mo – ment to a – rise.
mo – ment

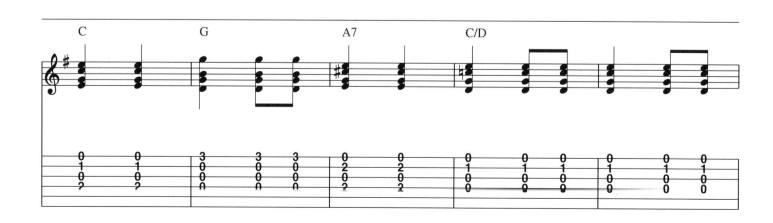

C   G   A7   C/D

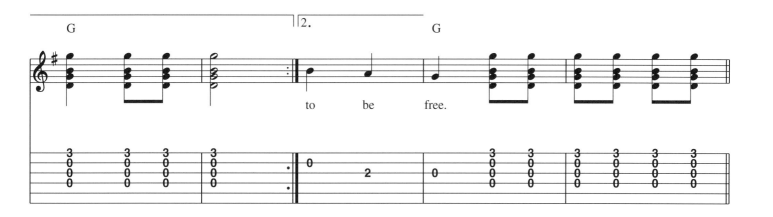

Chorus

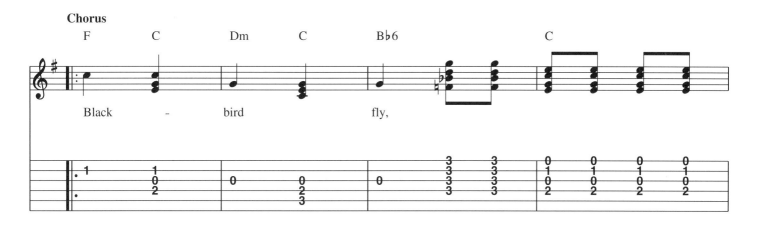

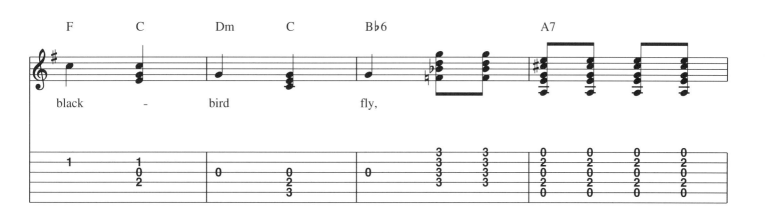

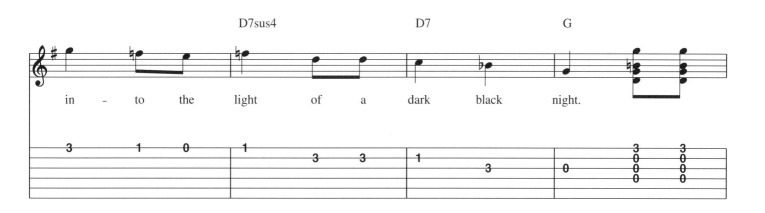

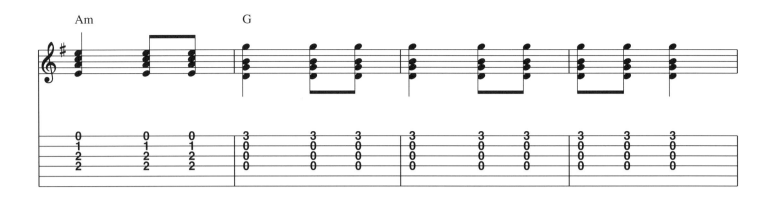

Verse

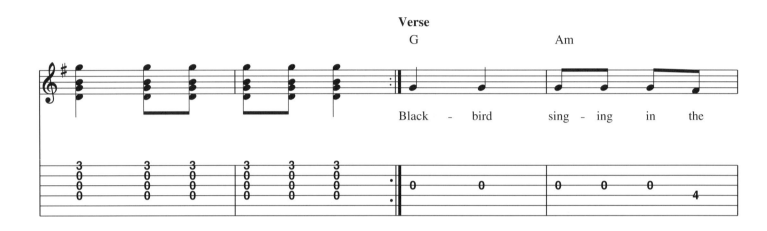

Black - bird sing - ing in the

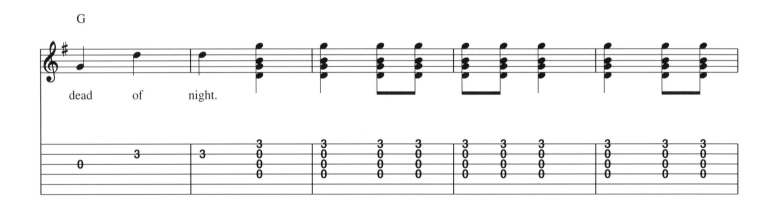

dead of night.

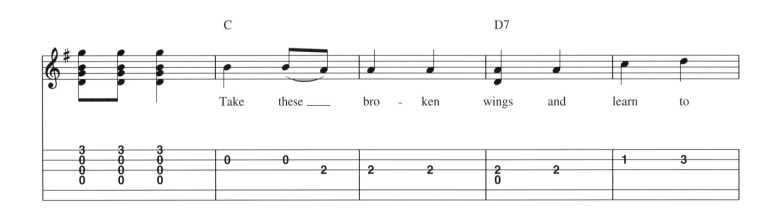

Take these ____ bro - ken wings and learn to

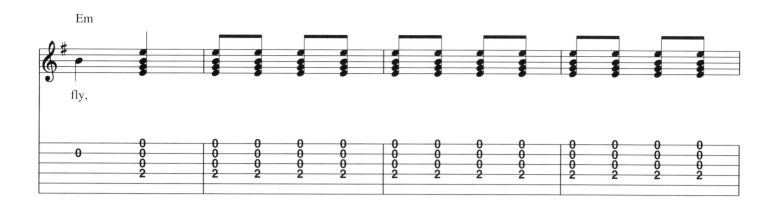

fly,

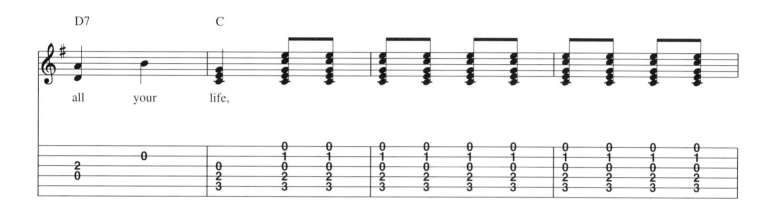

all   your   life,

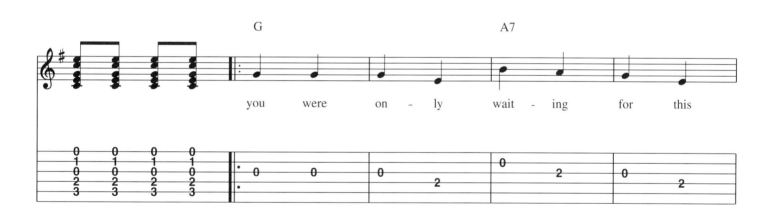

you   were   on - ly   wait - ing   for   this

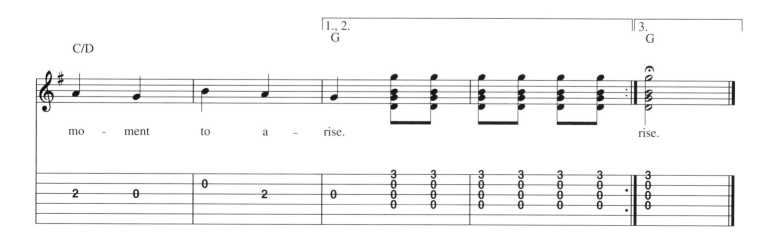

mo - ment   to   a - rise.   rise.

Blue Suede Shoes

Words and Music by Carl Lee Perkins

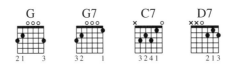

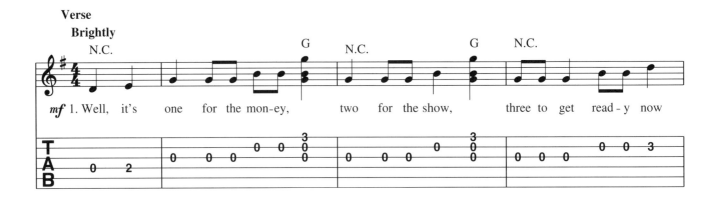

Strum Pattern: 2, 3
Pick Pattern: 3, 4

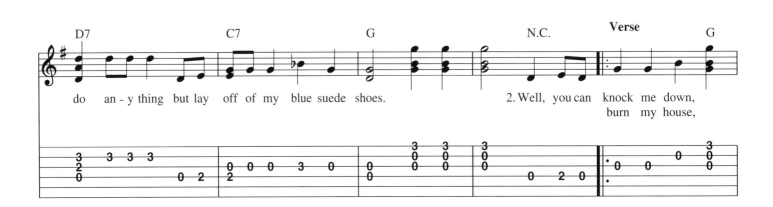

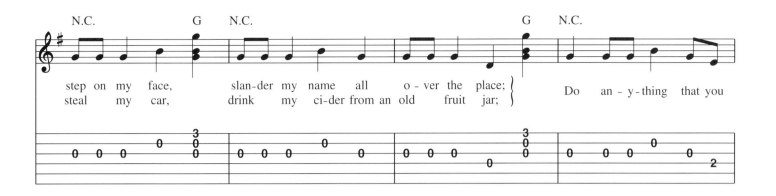

step on my face, / steal my car, slan-der my name all o - ver the place; / drink my ci-der from an old fruit jar; Do an - y-thing that you

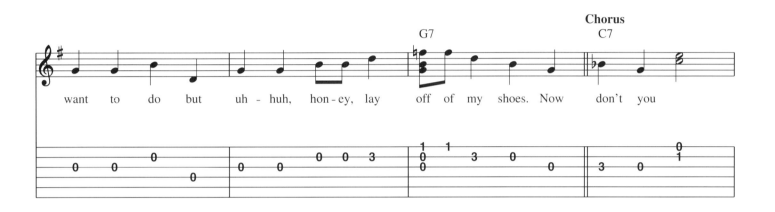

Chorus

want to do but uh - huh, hon - ey, lay off of my shoes. Now don't you

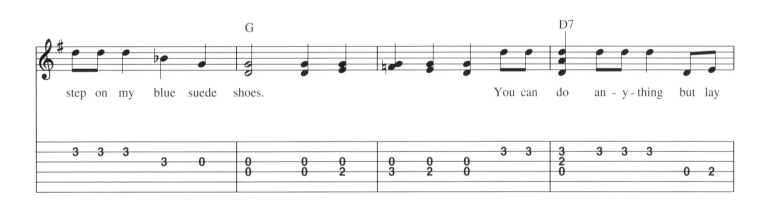

step on my blue suede shoes. You can do an - y-thing but lay

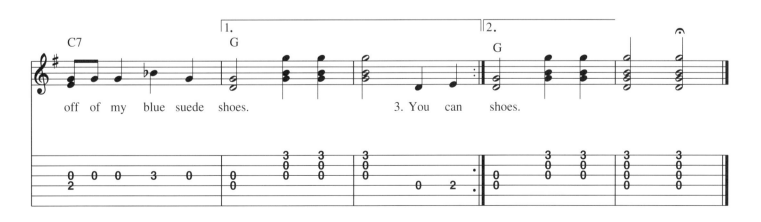

off of my blue suede shoes. 3. You can shoes.

Born to Be Wild

Words and Music by Mars Bonfire

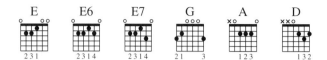

Strum Pattern: 2, 4
Pick Pattern: 3, 4

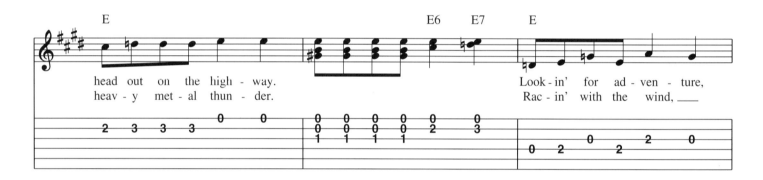

MCA Music Publishing

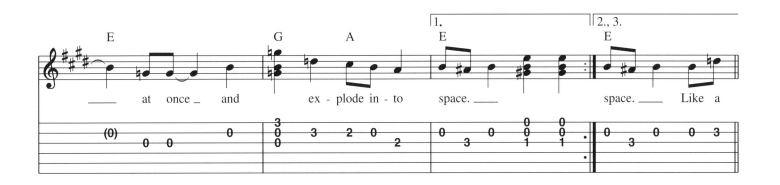

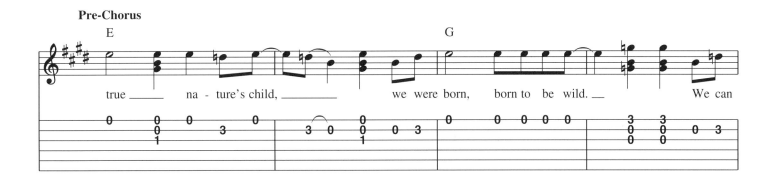

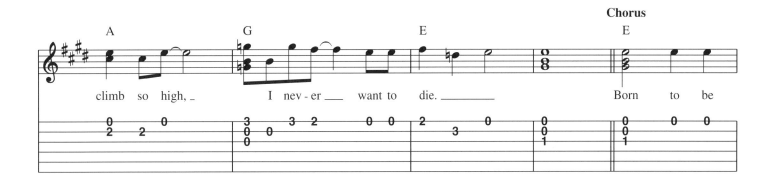

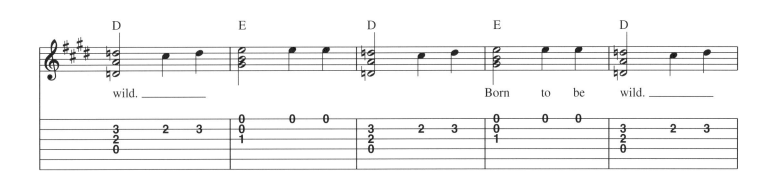

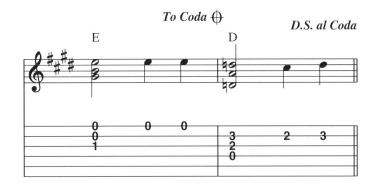

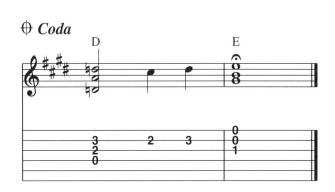

The Boys Are Back in Town

Words and Music by Philip Parris-Lynott

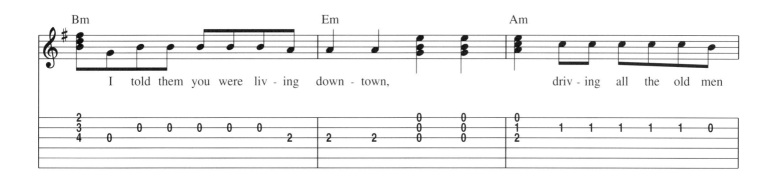

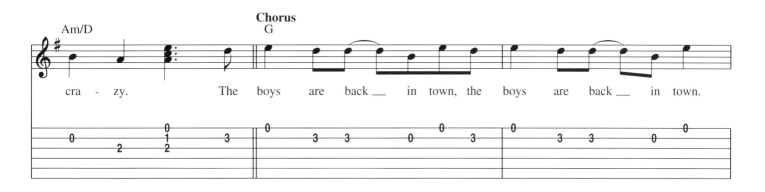

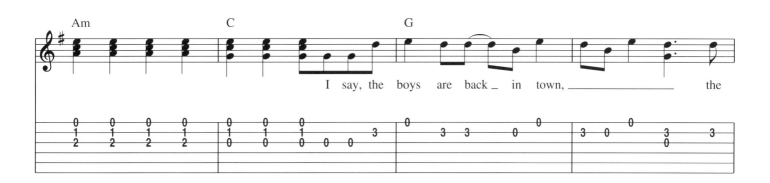

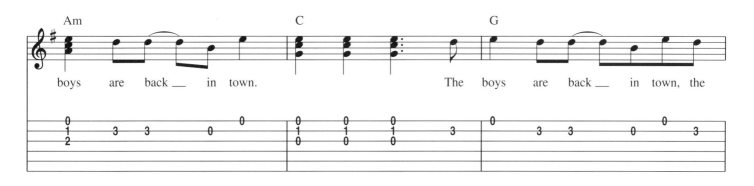

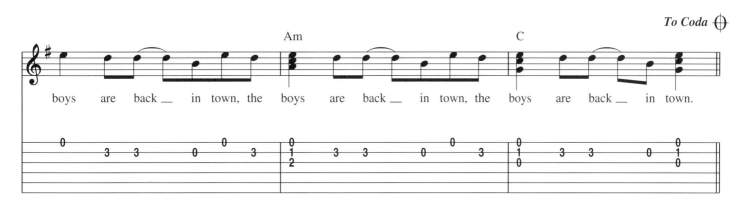

Interlude

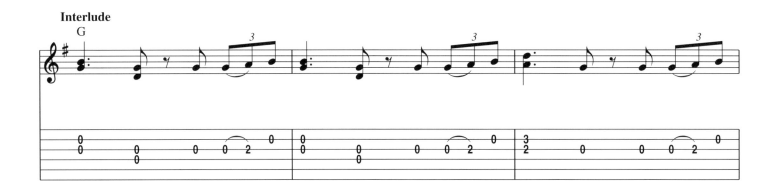

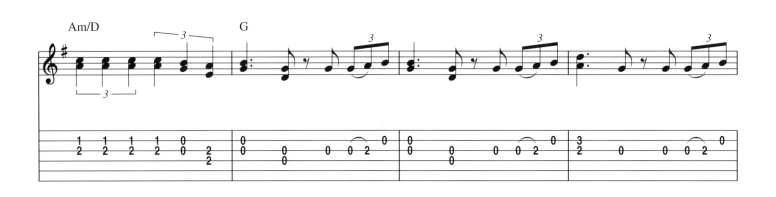

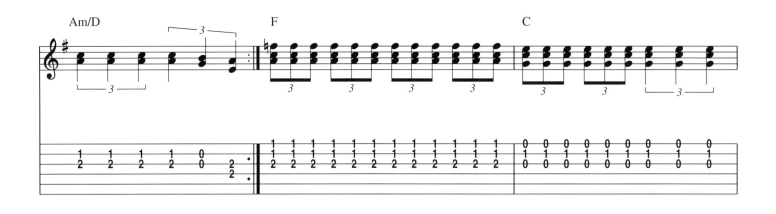

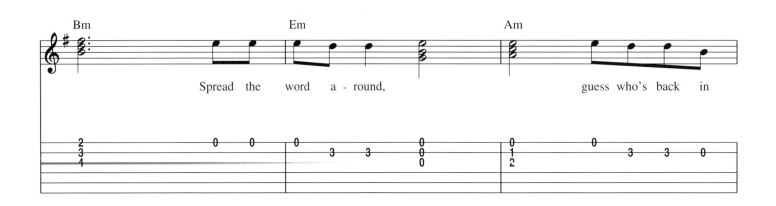

Spread the word a - round, guess who's back in

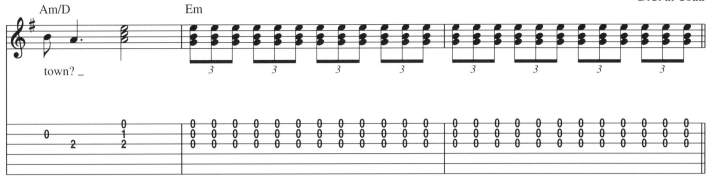

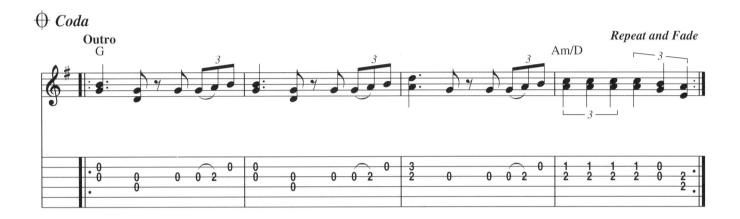

Additional Lyrics

2. You know that chick that used to dance a lot?
   Every night she'd be on the floor shaking what she'd got.
   Man, when I tell you she was cool, she was hot,
   I mean she was steaming.
   And that time over at Johnny's place,
   Well, this chick got up and she slapped Johnny's face.
   Man, we just fell about the place,
   If that chick don't wanna know, forget her.

3. Friday night they'll be dressed to kill
   Down at Dino's Bar and Grill.
   The drink will flow and blood will spill,
   And if the boys want to fight, you better let 'em.
   That jukebox in the corner blasting out my favorite song.
   The nights are getting warmer, it won't be long.
   It won't be long till summer comes
   Now that the boys are here again.

California Dreamin'

Words and Music by John Phillips and Michelle Phillips

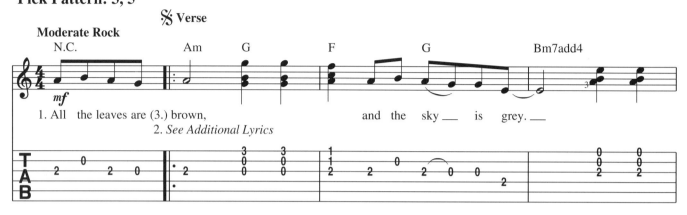

Strum Pattern: 3, 6
Pick Pattern: 3, 5

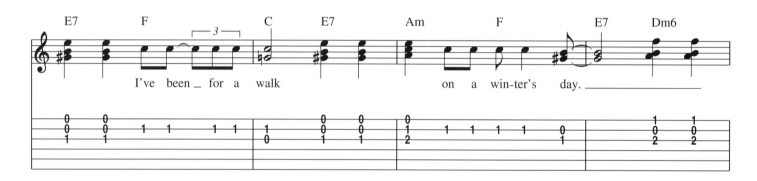

1. All the leaves are (3.) brown, and the sky is grey.
2. *See Additional Lyrics*

I've been for a walk on a win-ter's day.

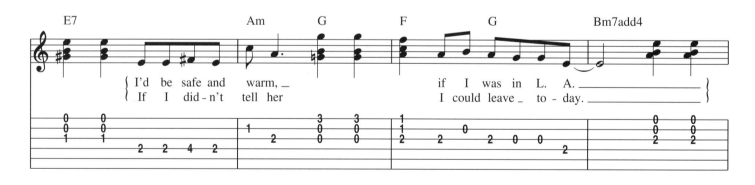

{ I'd be safe and warm, if I was in L. A.
If I did-n't tell her I could leave to-day.

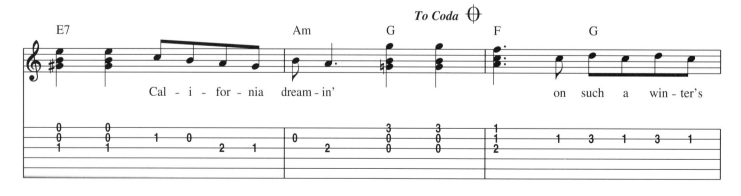

Cal-i-for-nia dream-in' on such a win-ter's

MCA Music Publishing

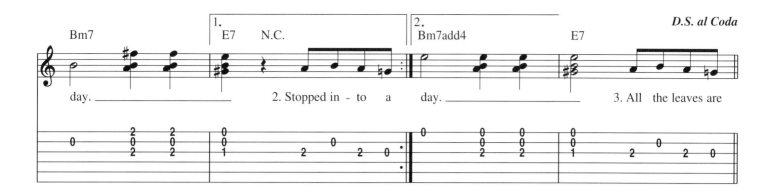

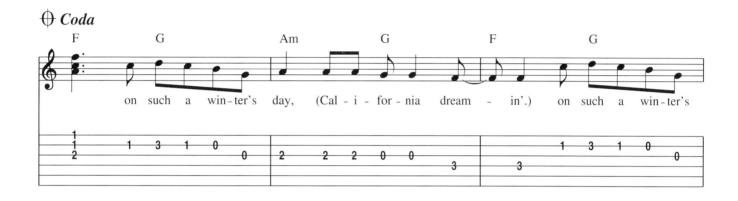

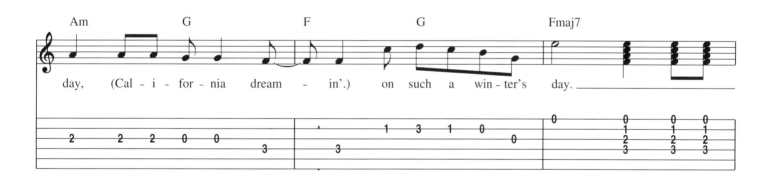

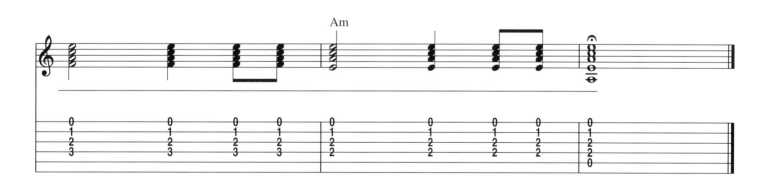

Additional Lyrics

2. Stopped into a church I passed along the way.
   Oh, I got down on my knees, and I pretend to pray.
   You know the preacher likes the cold; he knows I'm gonna stay.
   California dreamin', on such a winter's day.

California Girls

Words and Music by Brian Wilson and Mike Love

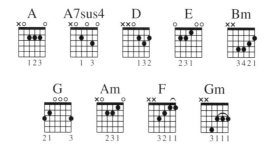

Strum Pattern: 1, 2
Pick Pattern: 2, 4

Intro
Moderately

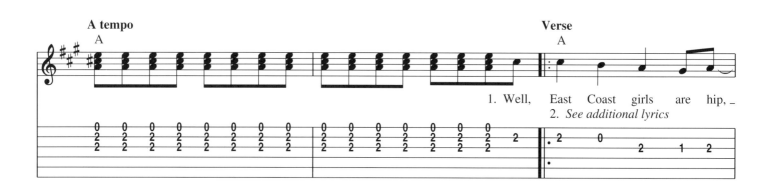

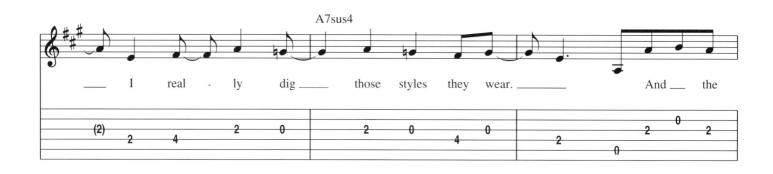

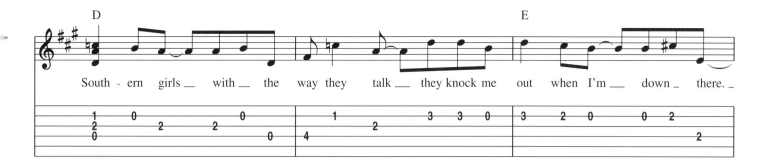

Southern girls _ with _ the way they talk _ they knock me out when I'm _ down _ there. _

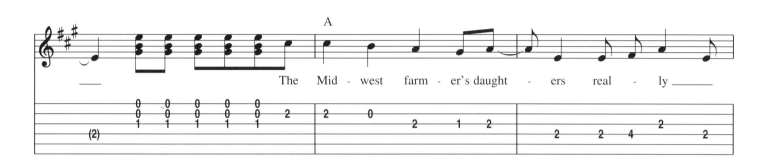

_ The Midwest farmer's daughters really ____

make you feel alright. ____ And _ the Northern girls _ with _ the

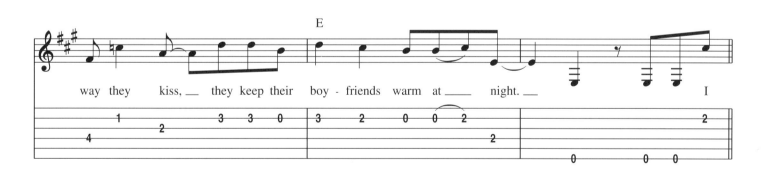

way they kiss, _ they keep their boyfriends warm at ____ night. _

Chorus

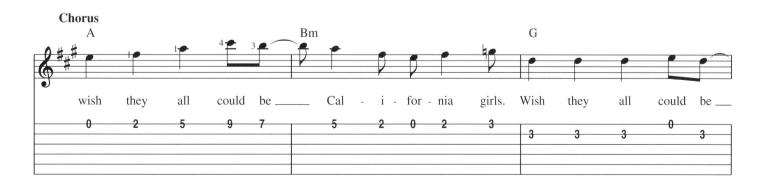

wish they all could be ____ California girls. Wish they all could be _

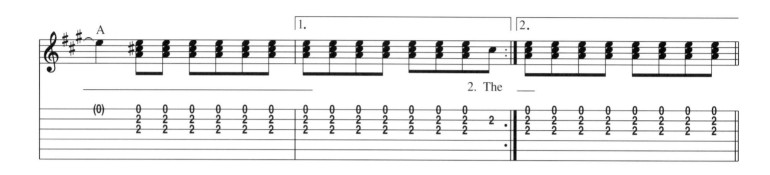

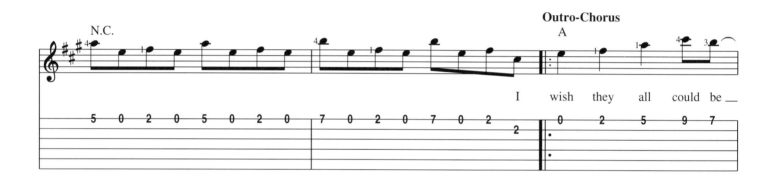

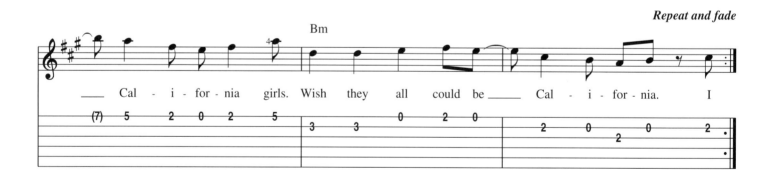

Additional Lyrics

2. The West Coast has the sunshine,
   And the girls all get so tan.
   I dig a French bikini on Hawaiian islands dolls,
   By a palm tree in the sand.
   I been all around this great big world
   And I've seen all kinds of girls.
   Yeah, but I couldn't wait to get back in the states,
   Back to the cutest girls in the world.

Candle in the Wind

Words and Music by Elton John and Bernie Taupin

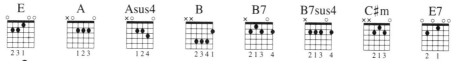

Strum Pattern: 3
Pick Pattern: 2

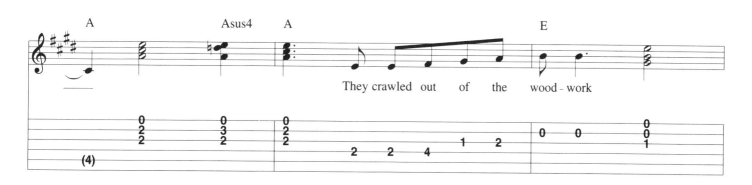

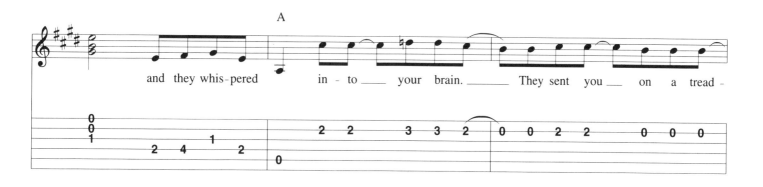

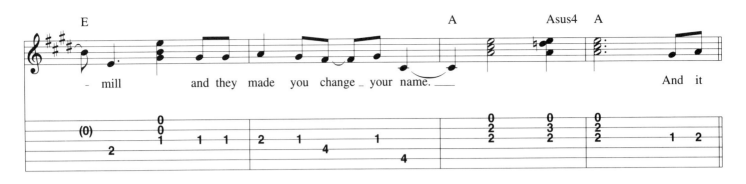

Chorus

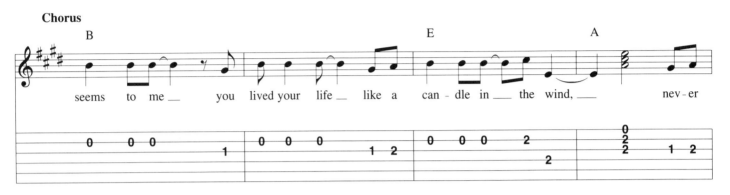

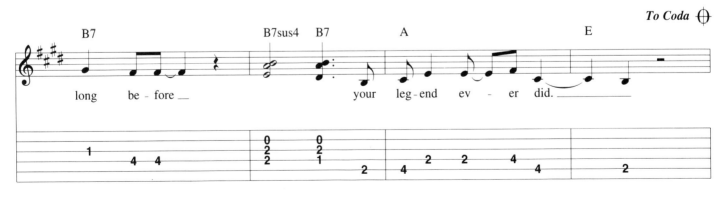

2nd time, D.C. al Coda

Additional Lyrics

2. Loneliness was tough, the toughest role you ever played.
   Hollywood created a superstar and pain was the price you paid.
   And even when you died, oh, the press still hounded you.
   All the papers had to say was that Marilyn was found in the nude.

3. Goodbye, Norma Jean. Though I never knew you at all,
   You had the grace to hold yourself while those around you crawled.
   Goodbye, Norma Jean, from a young man in the twenty second row,
   Who sees you as something more than sexual, more than just our Marilyn Monroe.

Change the World

Words and Music by Wayne Kirkpatrick, Gordon Kennedy and Tommy Sims

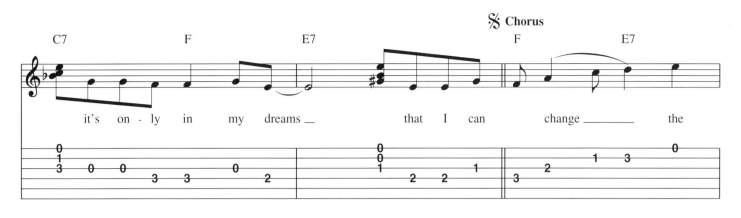

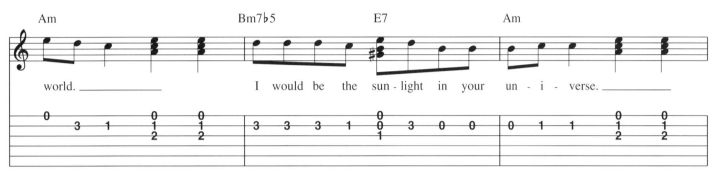

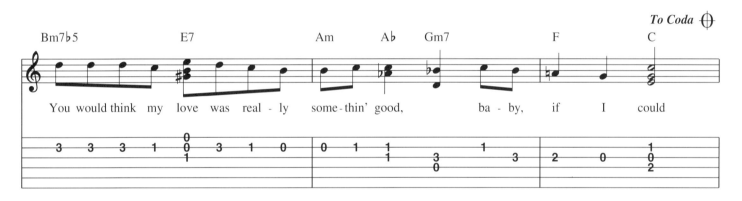

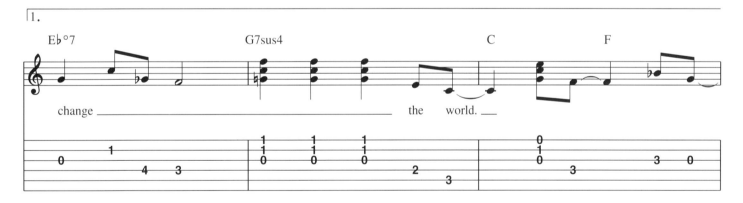

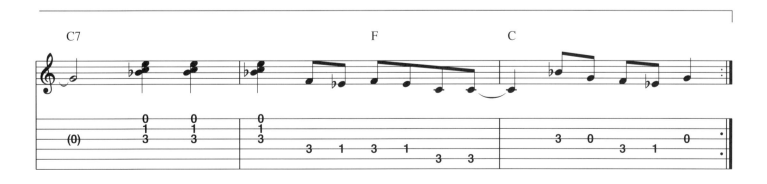

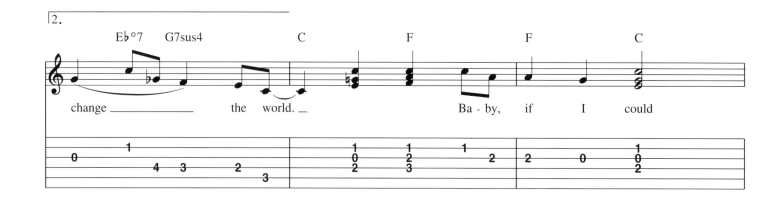

change _____ the world. _ Ba - by, if I could

D.S. al Coda

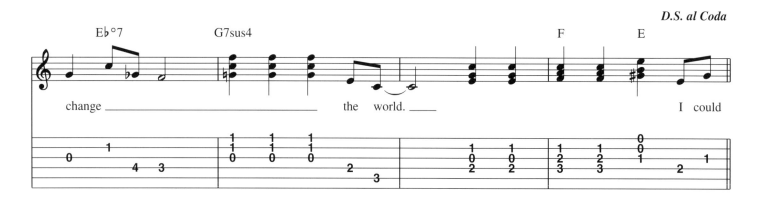

change _____ the world. _____ I could

Coda

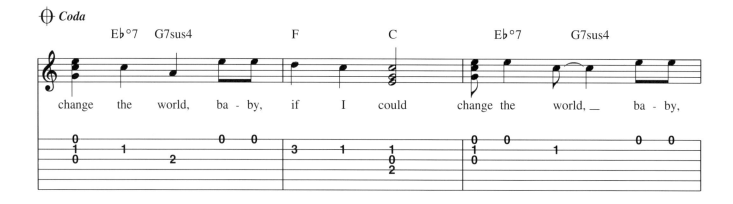

change the world, ba - by, if I could change the world, _ ba - by,

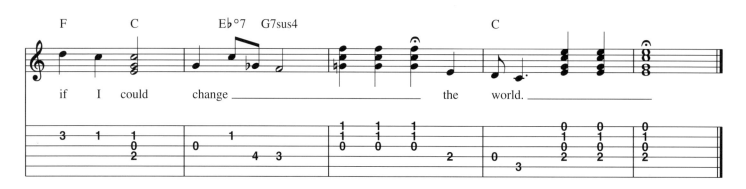

if I could change _____ the world. _____

Additional Lyrics

2. If I could be king
   Even for a day,
   I'd take you as my queen,
   I'd have it no other way.
   And our love would rule
   In this kingdom that we had made
   Till then I'll be a fool,
   Wishin' for the day...

Day Tripper

Words and Music by John Lennon and Paul McCartney

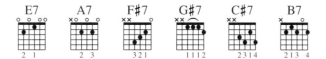

Strum Pattern: 2, 5
Pick Pattern: 4

Intro

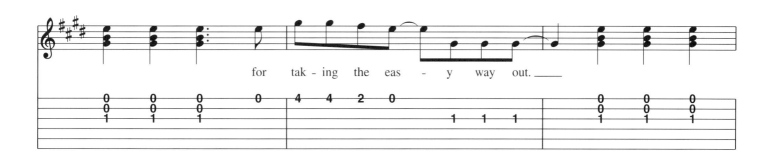

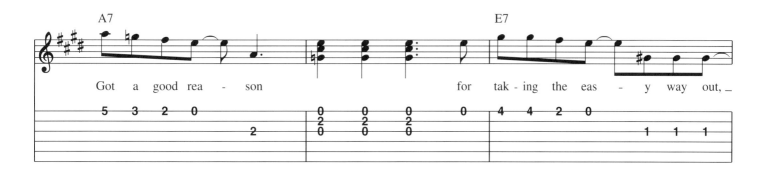

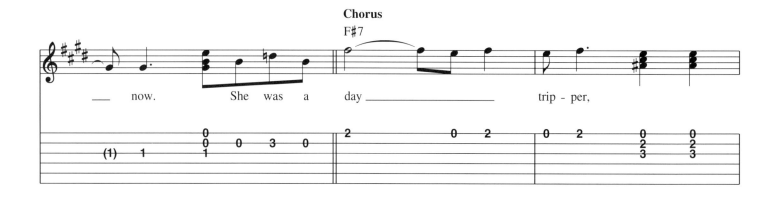

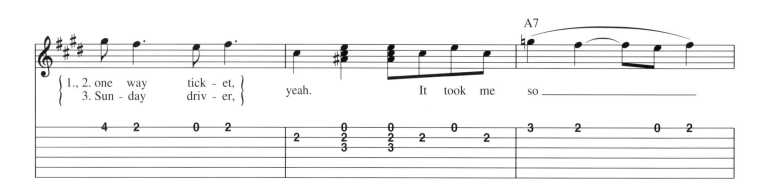

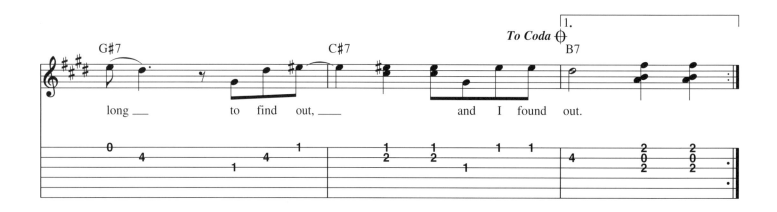

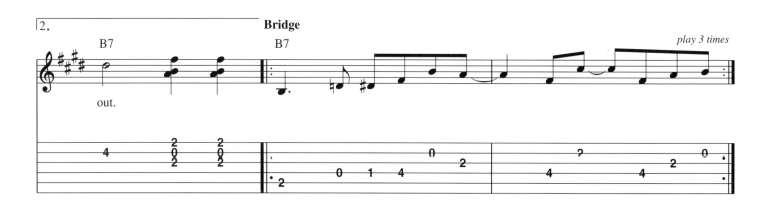

Guitar Solo

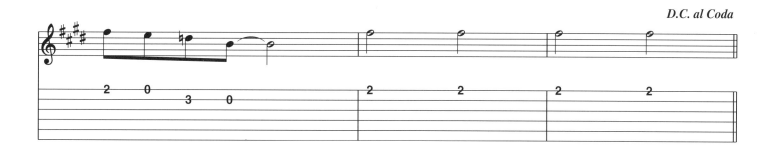

D.C. al Coda

out.

Outro

play 4 times

Day   trip-per,   day   trip-per,   yeah.

Repeat and Fade

Additional Lyrics

2. She's a big teaser.
    She took me half the way there.
    She's a big teaser.
    She took me half the way there, now.

3. Tried to please her.
    She only played one night stands.
    Tried to please her.
    She only played one night stands, now.

Crazy

Words and Music by Willie Nelson

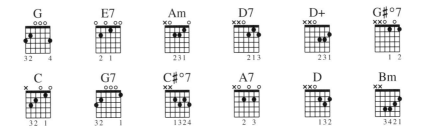

Strum Pattern: 4
Pick Pattern: 3

Verse
Moderately Slow

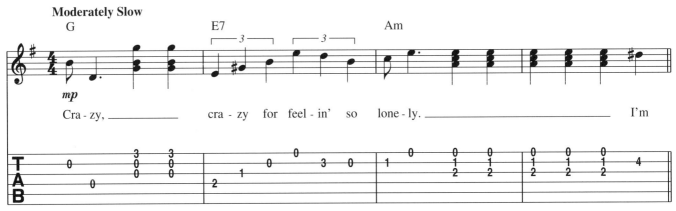

Cra - zy, _____ cra - zy for feel - in' so lone - ly. _____ I'm

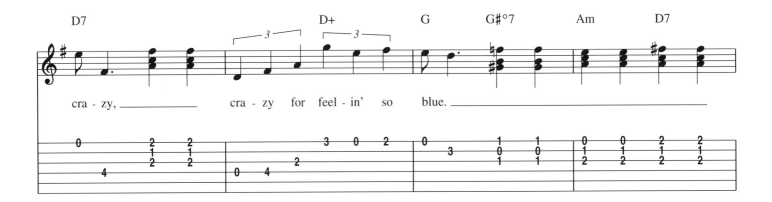

cra - zy, _____ cra - zy for feel - in' so blue. _____

I knew _____ you'd love me as long as you want - ed, _____ and then

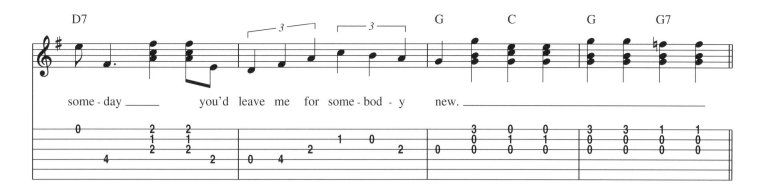

some - day _____ you'd leave me for some - bod - y new. _____

Bridge

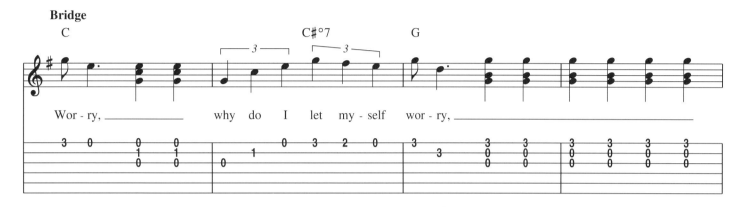

Wor - ry, _____ why do I let my - self wor - ry, _____

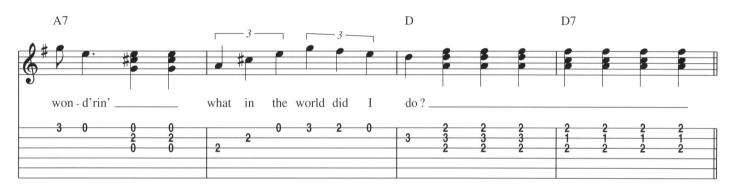

won - d'rin' _____ what in the world did I do? _____

Outro

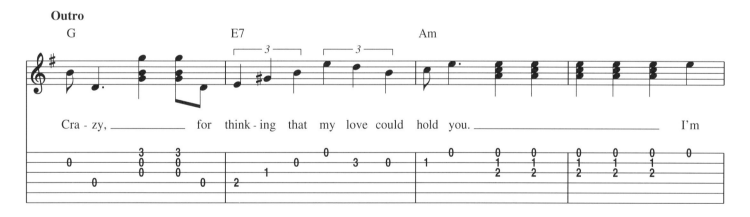

Cra - zy, _____ for think - ing that my love could hold you. _____ I'm

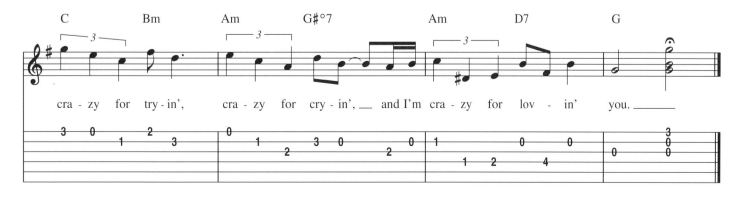

cra - zy for try - in', cra - zy for cry - in', ___ and I'm cra - zy for lov - in' you. _____

Do Wah Diddy Diddy

Words and Music by Jeff Barry and Ellie Greenwich

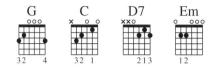

Strum Pattern: 1, 3
Pick Pattern: 2, 4

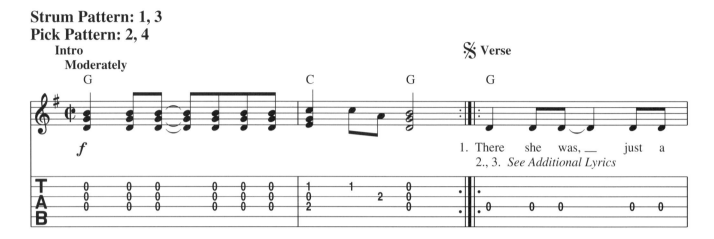

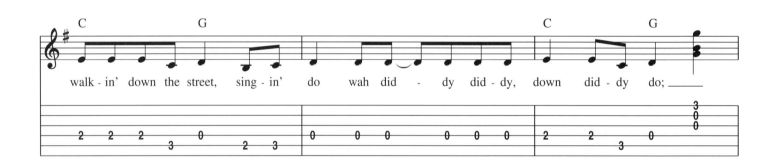

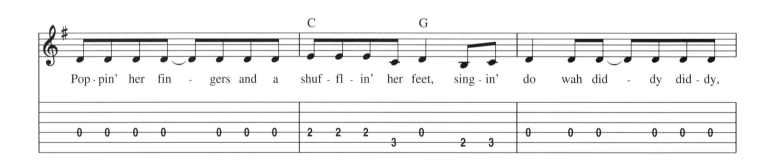

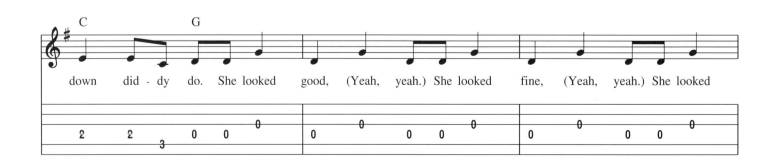

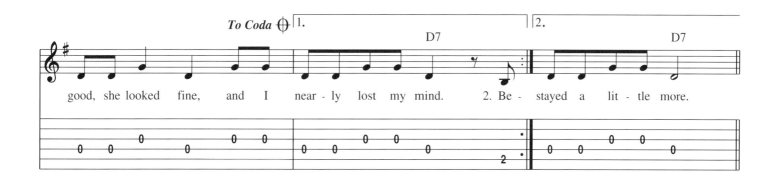

good, she looked fine, and I near-ly lost my mind. 2. Be - stayed a lit - tle more.

Bridge

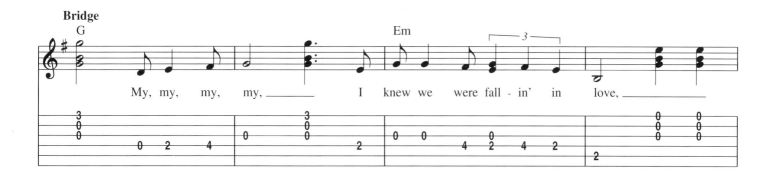

My, my, my, my, _____ I knew we were fall - in' in love, _____

D.S. al Coda

My, my, my, my, _____ I told her all the things I was dream - in' of. _____ 3. Now,

⊕ **Coda**

Outro   *Repeat and Fade*

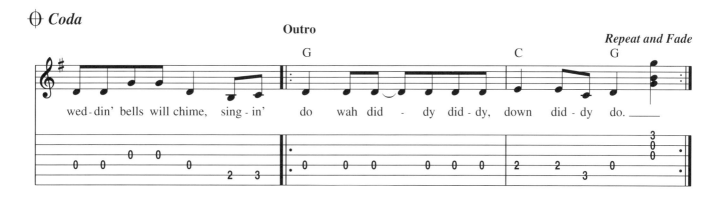

wed - din' bells will chime, sing - in' do wah did - dy did - dy, down did - dy do. _____

Additional Lyrics

2. Before I knew it she was walkin' next to me,
   Singin' do wah diddy diddy, down diddy do;
   She took my hand just as nat'ral as can be,
   Singin' do wah diddy diddy, down diddy do.
   We walked on, (Yeah, yeah.)
   To my door. (Yeah, yeah.)
   We walked on to my door,
   And she stayed a little more.

3. Now, we're together nearly ev'ry single day,
   Singin' do wah diddy diddy, down diddy do.
   We're so happy and that's how we're gonna stay.
   Singin' do wah diddy diddy, down diddy do.
   'Cause I'm hers, (Yeah, yeah.)
   And she's mine. (Yeah, yeah.)
   Well, I'm hers and she's mine
   And the weddin' bells will chime.

Don't Look Back in Anger

Words and Music by Noel Gallagher

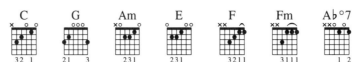

Strum Pattern: 4
Pick Pattern: 1

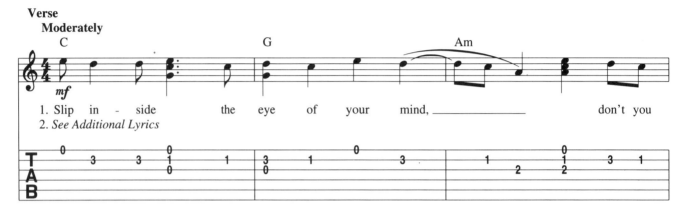

1. Slip in - side the eye of your mind, _____ don't you
2. *See Additional Lyrics*

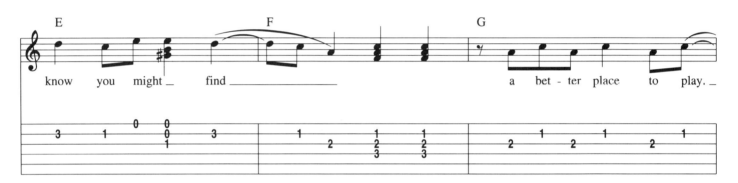

know you might _ find _____ a bet - ter place to play. _

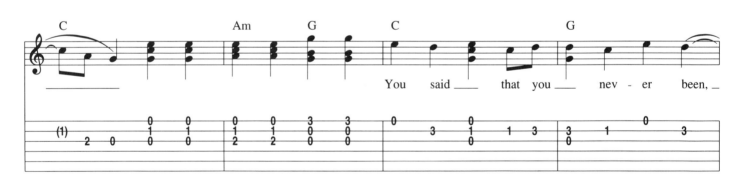

You said _ that you _ nev - er been, _

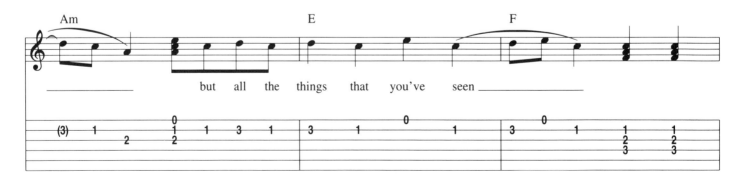

but all the things that you've seen _____

you ain't ev - er gon - na burn ___ my ___ heart ___ out. ___

𝄋 **Chorus**

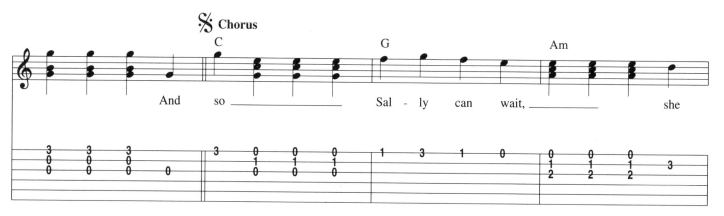

And so ___ Sal - ly can wait, ___ she

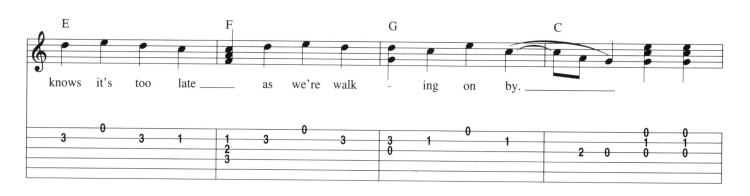

knows it's too late ___ as we're walk - ing on by. ___

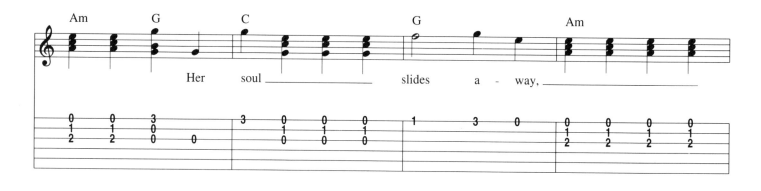

Her soul ___ slides a - way, ___

Additional Lyrics

2. Take me to the place where you go
   Where nobody knows if it's night or day
   But please don't put your life in the hands
   Of a rock 'n' roll band who'll throw it all away.

Pre-Chorus I'm gonna start a revolution from my bed
   'Cause you said the brains I had went to my head.
   Step outside 'cause summertime's in bloom.
   Stand up beside the fireplace, take that look from your face
   'Cause you ain't never gonna burn my heart out.

Ebony and Ivory

Words and Music by McCartney

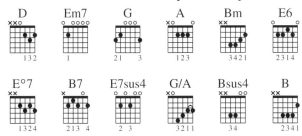

Strum Pattern: 1, 4
Pick Pattern: 1, 2

Chorus
Moderately

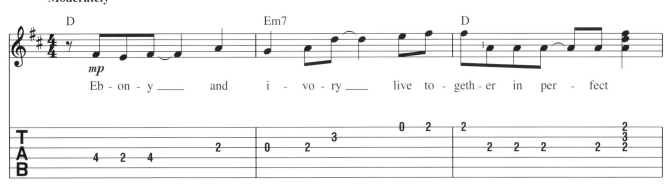

Eb - on - y ___ and i - vo - ry ___ live to - geth - er in per - fect

har - mo - ny, ___ side by side on my pian - o key - board, oh ___ Lord,

To Coda 1

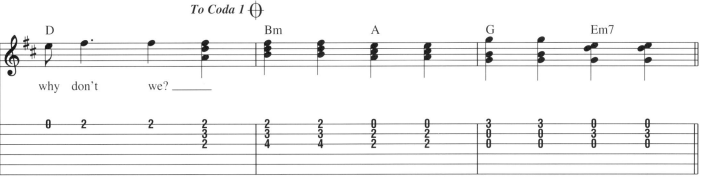

why don't we? _____

Verse

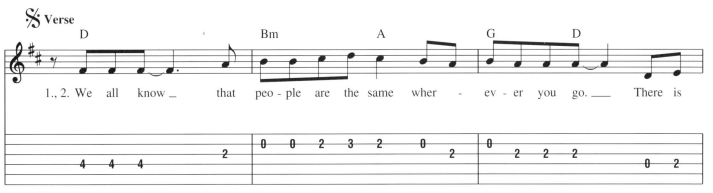

1., 2. We all know ___ that peo - ple are the same wher - ev - er you go. ___ There is

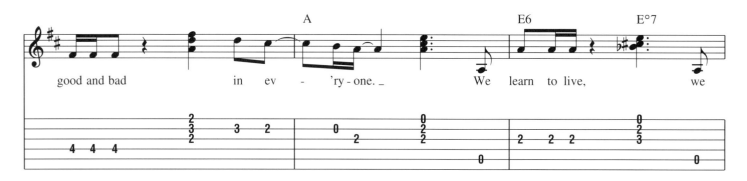

good and bad in ev-'ry-one. __ We learn to live, we

1st time, D.C. al Coda 1
2nd time, To Coda 2

learn to give each oth-er what we need __ to sur-vive __ to-geth-er a-live. _____

Coda 1

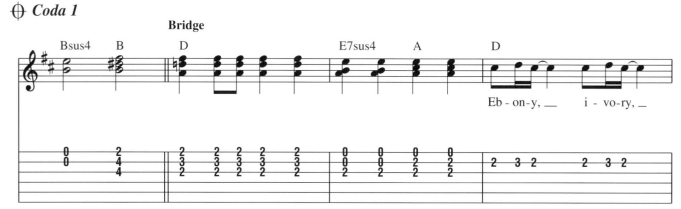

Bridge

Eb-on-y, __ i-vo-ry, __

D.S. al Coda 2

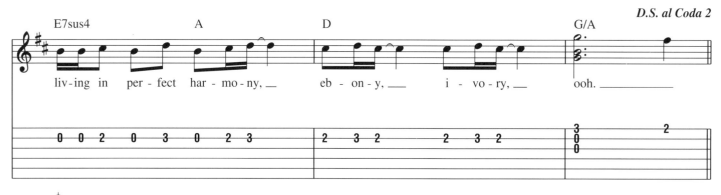

liv-ing in per-fect har-mo-ny, __ eb-on-y, __ i-vo-ry, __ ooh. _____

Coda 2

Chorus

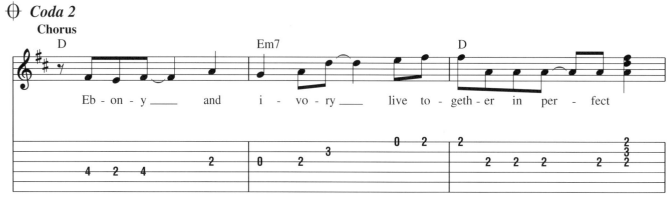

Eb-on-y _____ and i-vo-ry _____ live to-geth-er in per-fect

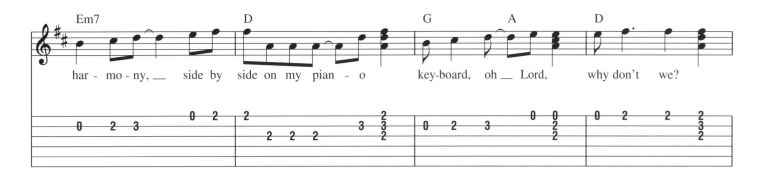

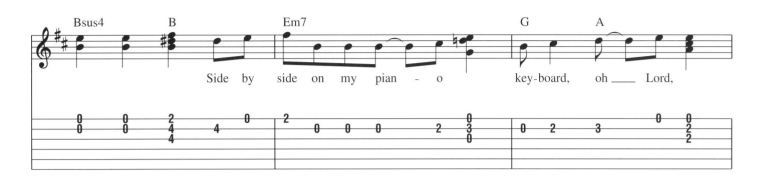

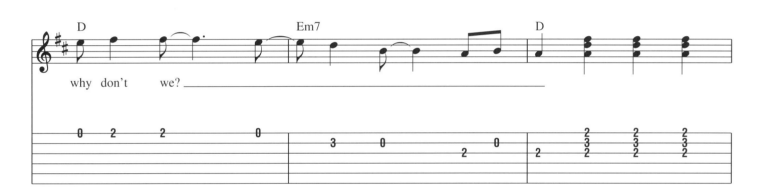

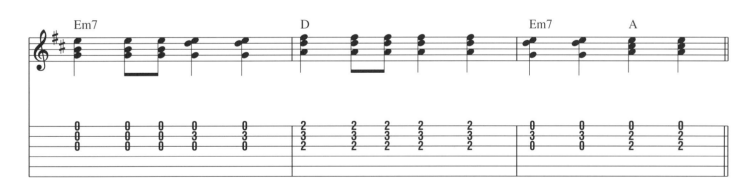

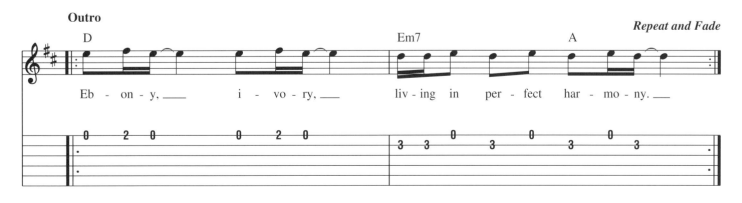

Every Breath You Take

Written and Composed by Sting

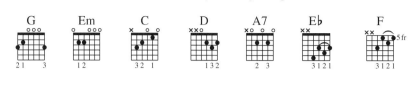

Strum Pattern: 4
Pick Pattern: 3

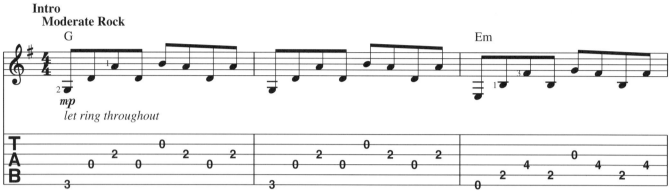

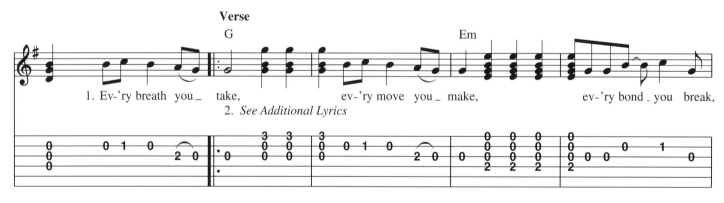

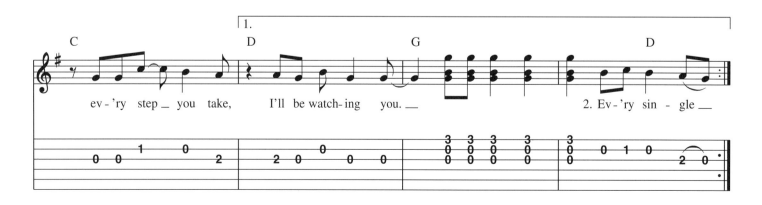

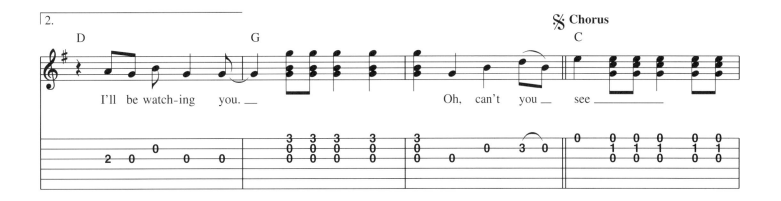

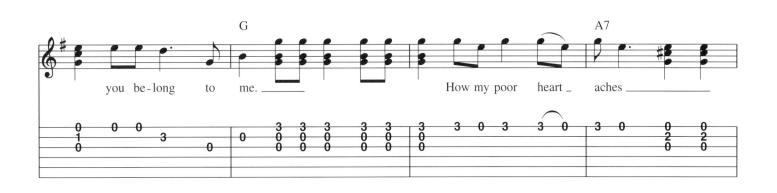

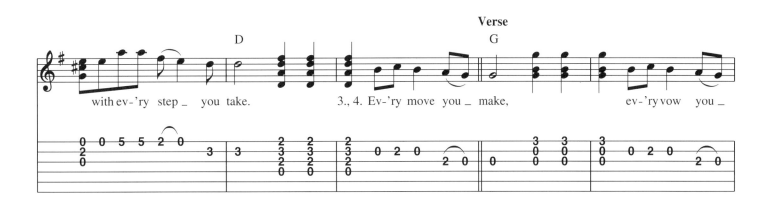

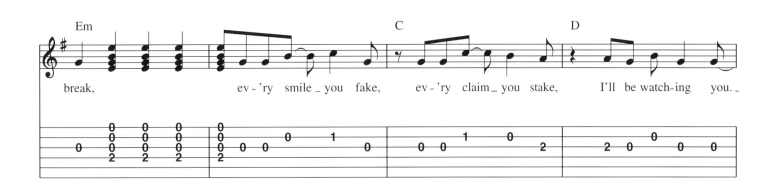

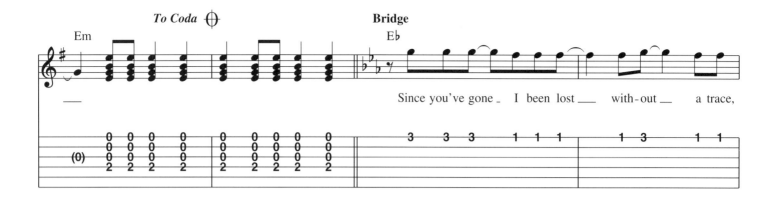

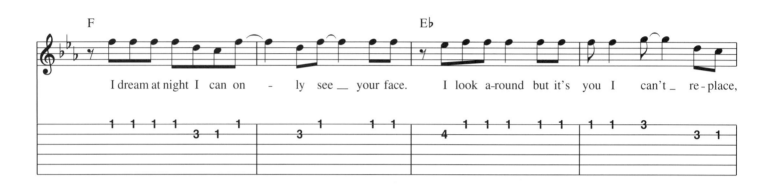

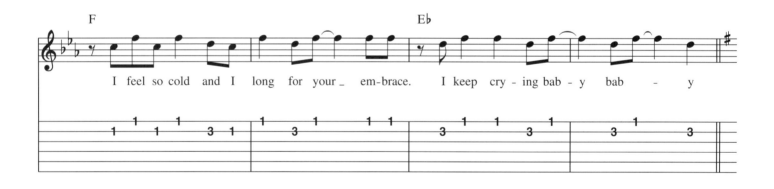

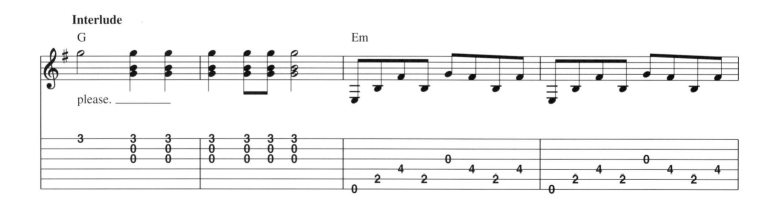

Oh can't you —

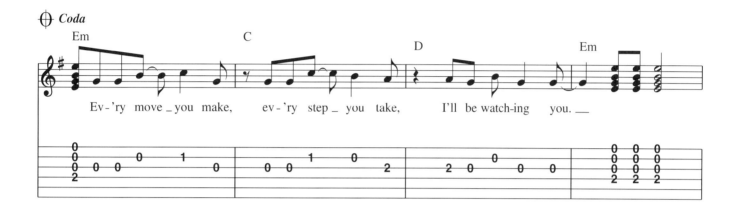

Ev-'ry move _ you make, ev-'ry step _ you take, I'll be watch-ing you. _

I'll be watch-ing you. _____

Additional Lyrics

2. Ev'ry single day, ev'ry word you say,
   Ev'ry game you play, ev'ry night you stay,
   I'll be watching you.

Everyday (I Have the Blues)

Words and Music by Peter Chatman

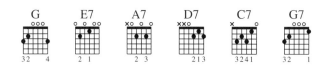

Strum Pattern: 2, 3
Pick Pattern: 2, 4

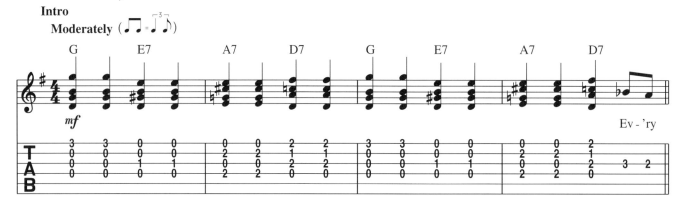

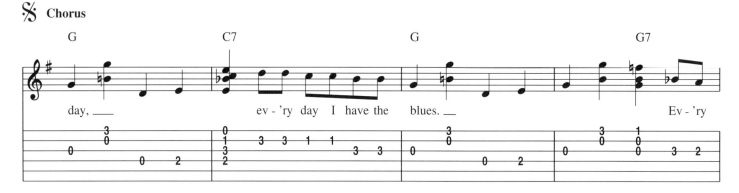

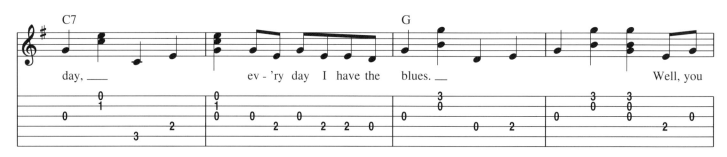

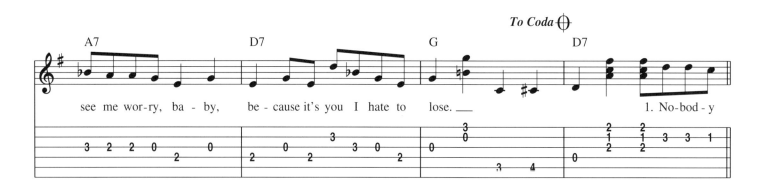

Verse

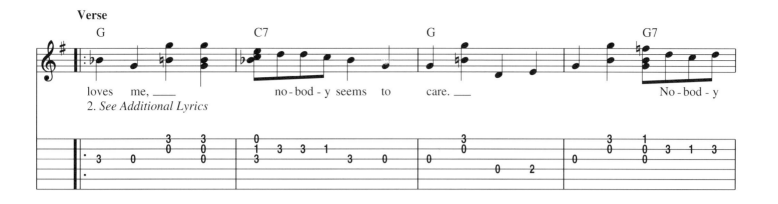

loves me, ____ no-bod-y seems to care. ____ No-bod-y
2. *See Additional Lyrics*

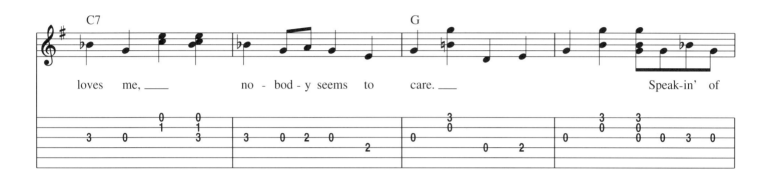

loves me, ____ no - bod - y seems to care. ____ Speak-in' of

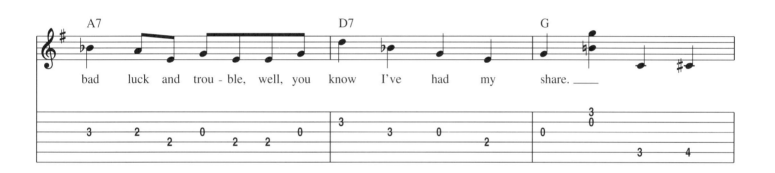

bad luck and trou - ble, well, you know I've had my share. ____

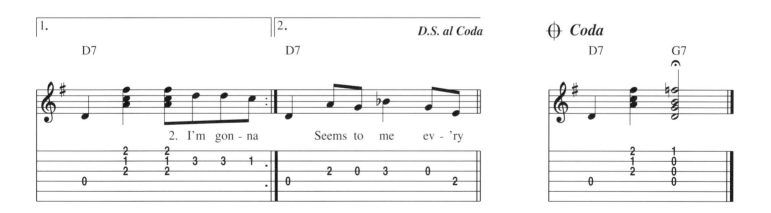

1. **2.** ***D.S. al Coda*** ⊕ *Coda*

2. I'm gon - na Seems to me ev - 'ry

Additional Lyrics

2. I'm gonna pack my suitcase, movin' on down the line.
Oh, I'm gonna pack my suitcase, move on down the line.
Well, there ain't nobody worryin' and there ain't nobody cryin'.

Free Bird

Words and Music by Allen Collins and Ronnie Van Zant

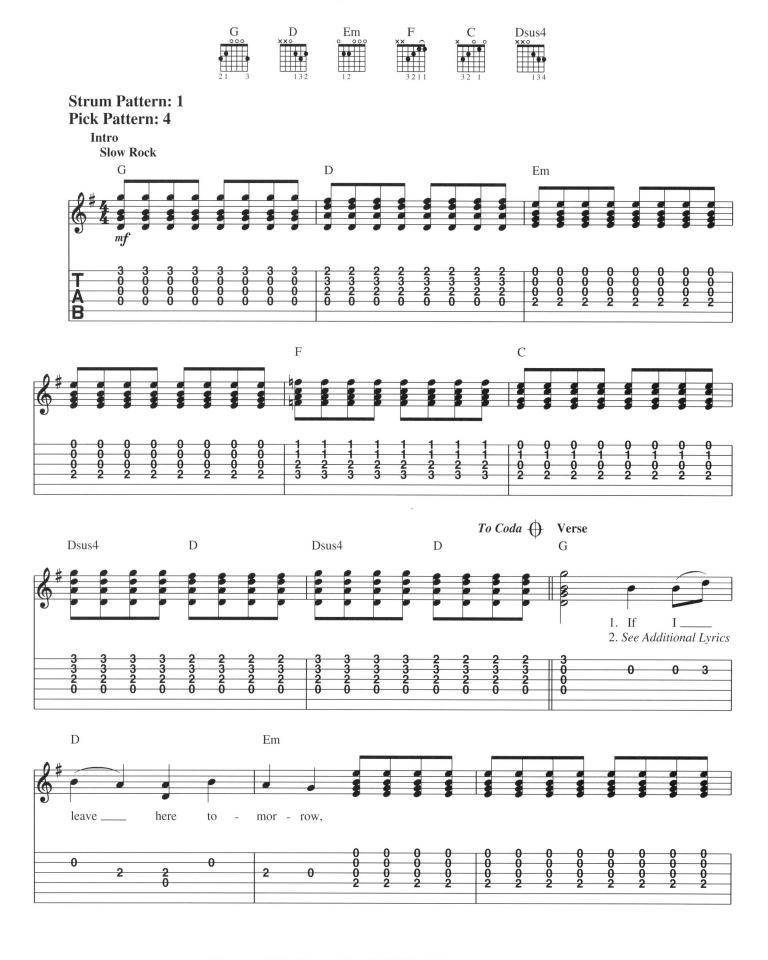

MCA Music Publishing

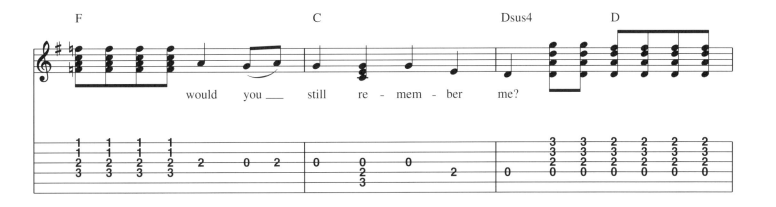

would you ___ still re - mem - ber me?

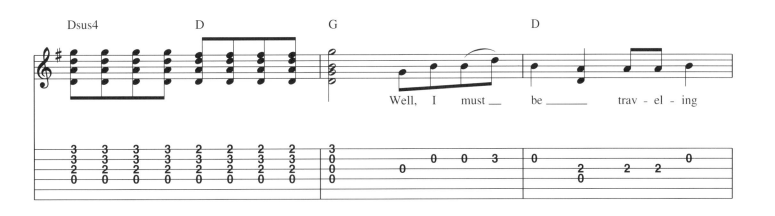

Well, I must ___ be ___ trav - el - ing

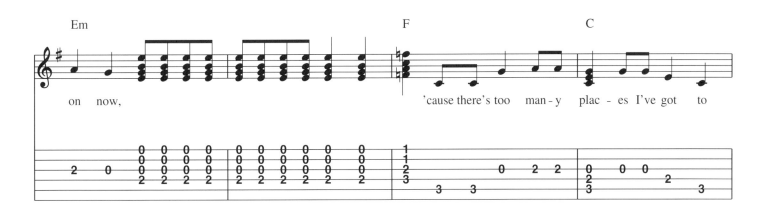

on now, 'cause there's too man - y plac - es I've got to

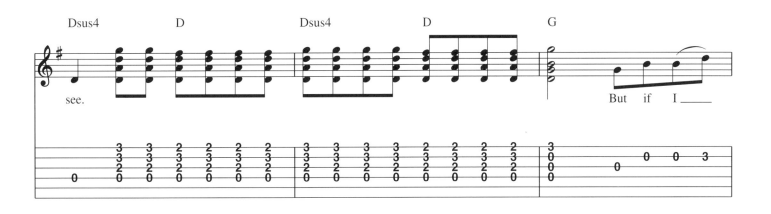

see. But if I ___

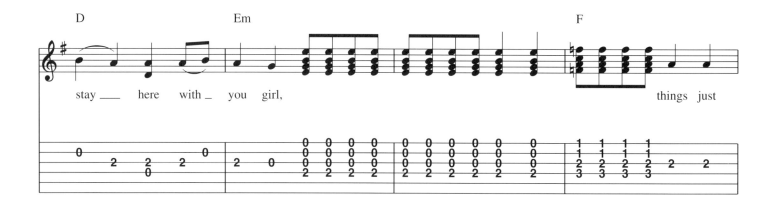

stay ___ here with _ you girl, things just

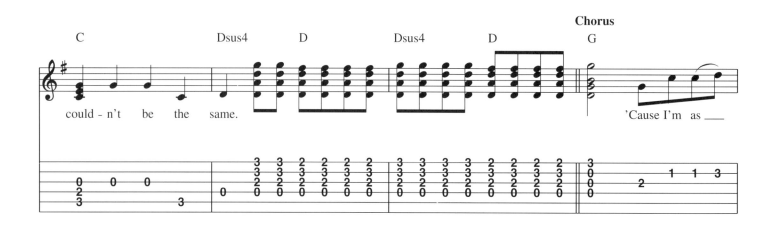

could - n't be the same. 'Cause I'm as ___

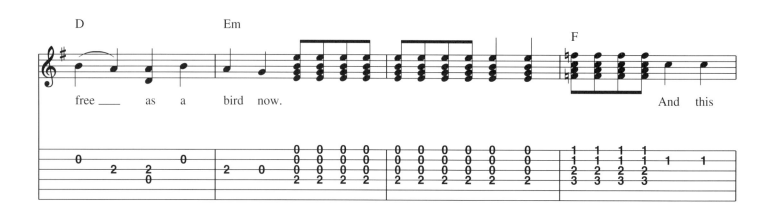

free ___ as a bird now. And this

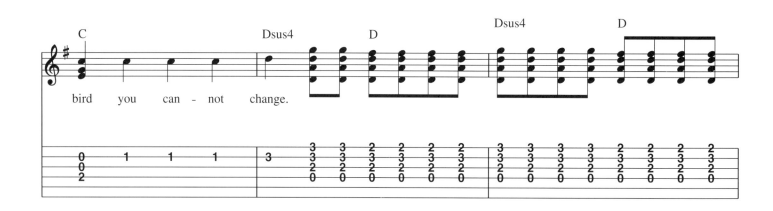

bird you can - not change.

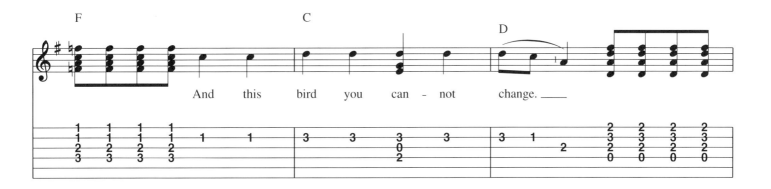

And this bird you can - not change. ____

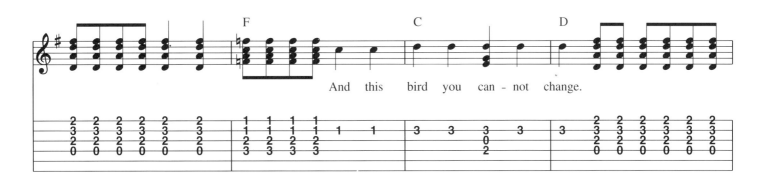

And this bird you can - not change.

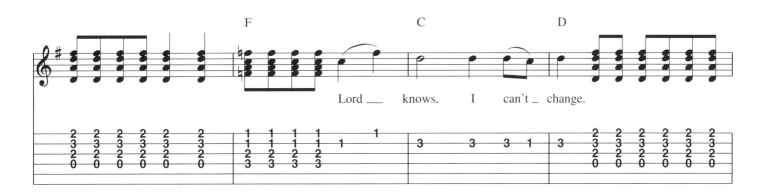

Lord ___ knows, I can't _ change.

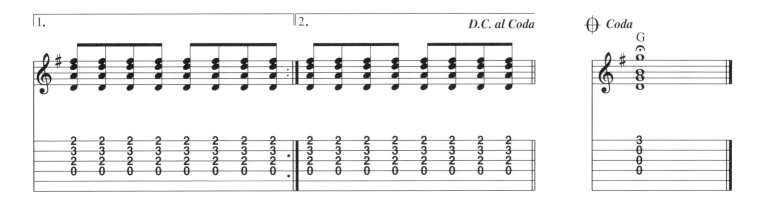

Additonal Lyrics

2. Bye, bye baby, it's been sweet now, yeah, yeah,
   Though this feelin' I can't change.
   A please don't take it so badly,
   'Cause the Lord knows I'm to blame.
   But if I stay here with you girl,
   Things just couldn't be the same.

Friends in Low Places

Words and Music by Dewayne Blackwell and Earl Bud Lee

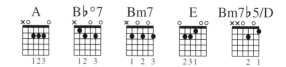

Strum Pattern: 1, 6
Pick Pattern: 2, 4

Intro
Moderately

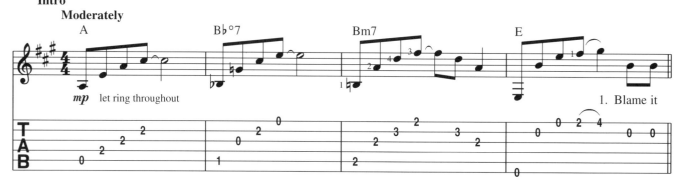

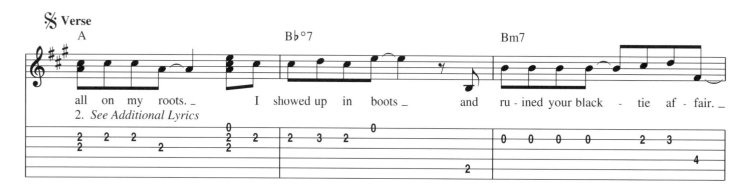

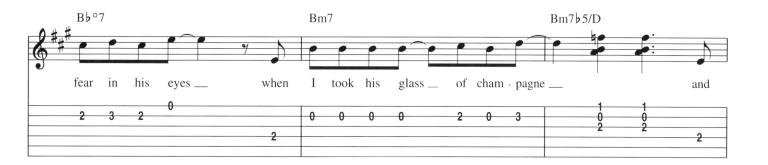

fear in his eyes __ when I took his glass __ of cham - pagne __ and

I toast - ed you, __ said, "Hon - ey, we may be through __ but you'll nev - er hear __ me com - plain." __

Chorus

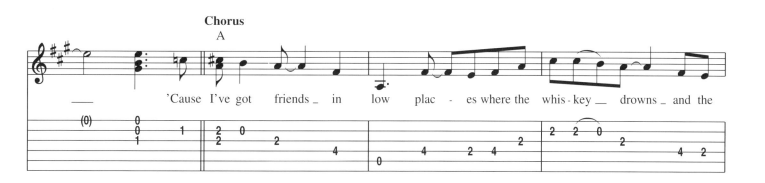

__ 'Cause I've got friends __ in low plac - es where the whis - key __ drowns __ and the

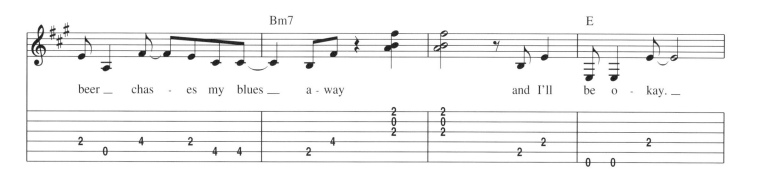

beer __ chas - es my blues __ a - way and I'll be o - kay. __

Yeah, I'm not big __ on so - cial grac - es. Think I'll

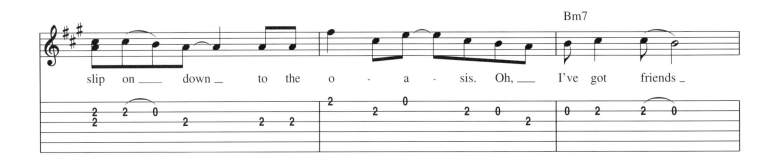

slip on ___ down _ to the o - a - sis. Oh, ___ I've got friends _

To Coda ⊕

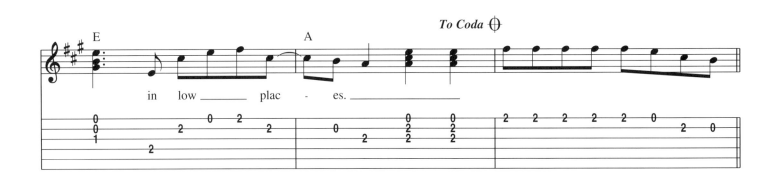

in low _____ plac - es. _____

Guitar Solo

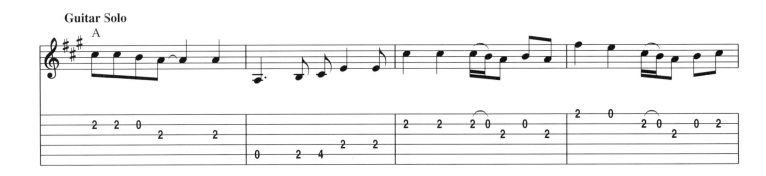

D.S. al Coda

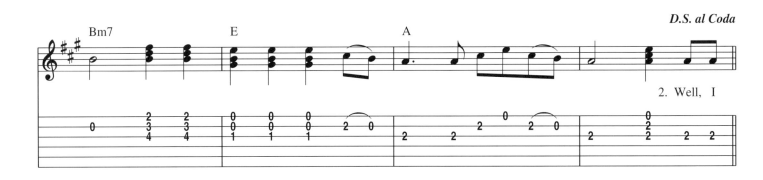

2. Well, I

⊕ *Coda*

Outro-Chorus

I've got friends _ in low plac - es where the

whis - key ___ drowns _ and the beer ___ chas - es my blues ___ a - way

and I'll be o - kay. ___ Yeah, I'm not big ___ on

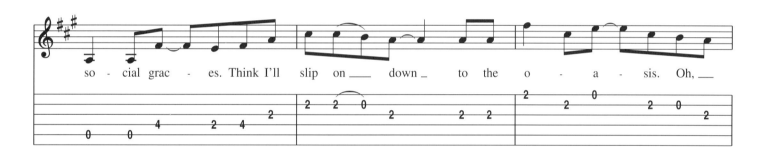

so - cial grac - es. Think I'll slip on ___ down _ to the o - a - sis. Oh, ___

Repeat and Fade

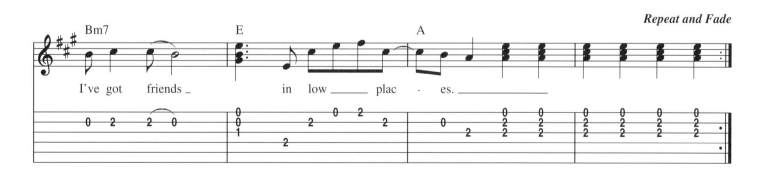

I've got friends _ in low _____ plac - es. _____

Additional Lyrics

2. Well, I guess I was wrong, I just don't belong,
   But then, I've been there before.
   Ev'rything's alright, I'll just say goodnight,
   And I'll show myself to the door.
   Hey, I didn't mean to cause a big scene,
   Just give me an hour and then,
   Well, I'll be as high as that ivory tower that you're livin' in.

From a Distance

Words and Music by Julie Gold

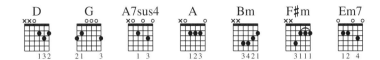

Strum Pattern: 2, 4
Pick Pattern: 1, 2

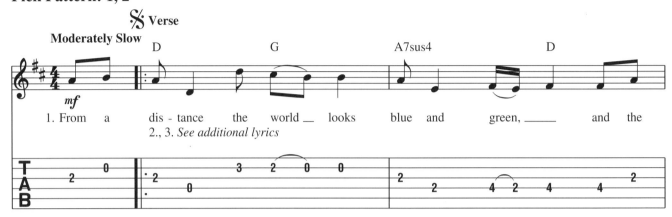

1. From a dis-tance the world __ looks blue and green, __ and the
2., 3. *See additional lyrics*

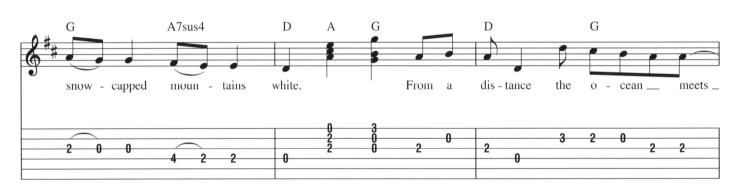

snow-capped moun-tains white. From a dis-tance the o-cean __ meets __

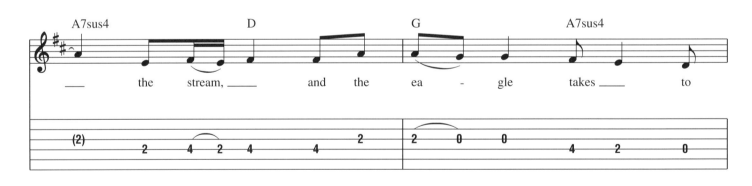

__ the stream, __ and the ea-gle takes __ to

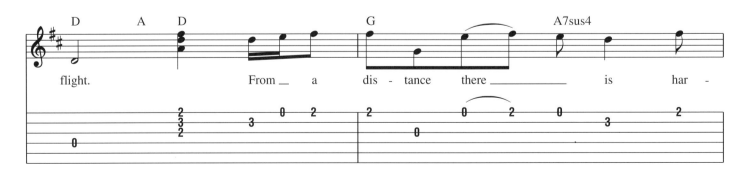

flight. From __ a dis-tance there _____ is har-

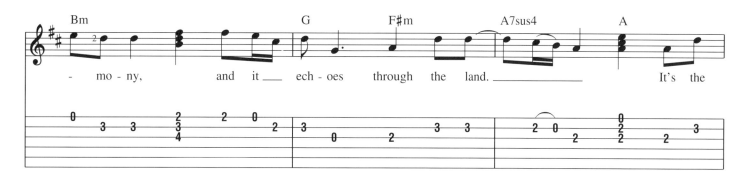

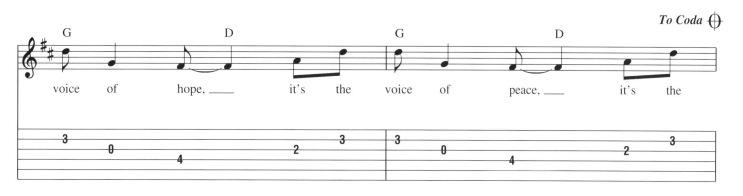

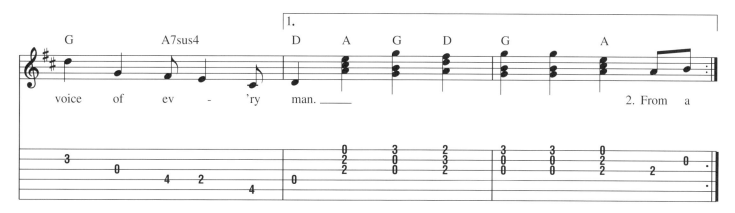

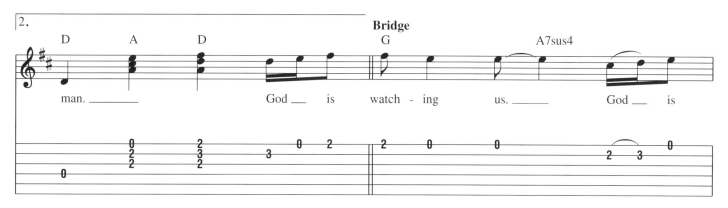

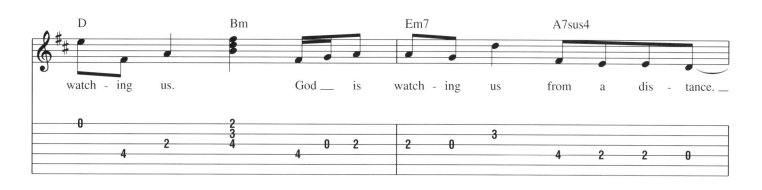

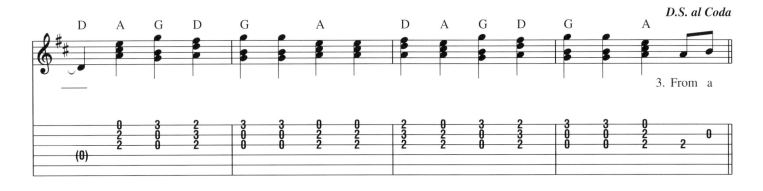

Coda

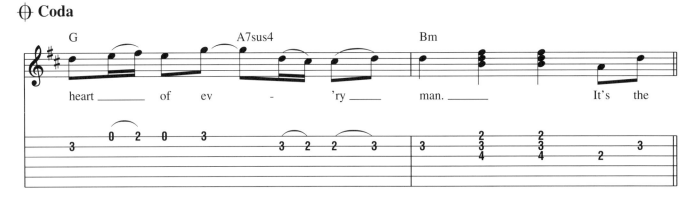

Outro

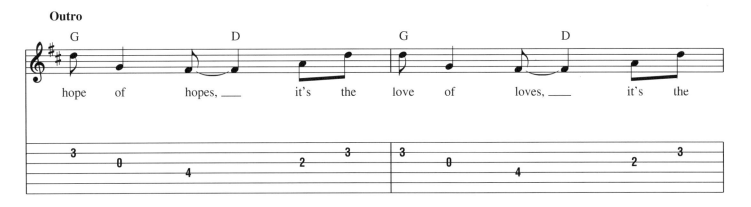

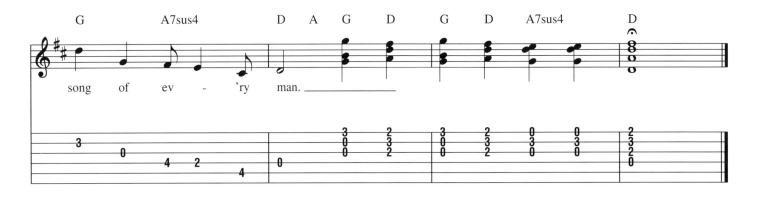

Additional Lyrics

2. From a distance we all have enough, and no one is in need.
   There are no guns, no bombs, no diseases, no hungry mouths to feed.
   From a distance we are instruments, marching in a common band.
   Playing songs of hope, playing songs of peace, they're the songs of ev'ry man.

3. From a distance you look like my friend, even though we are at war.
   From a distance I can't comprehend what all this war is for.
   From a distance there is harmony, and it echoes through the land.
   It's the hope of hopes, it's the love of loves, it's the heart of ev'ry man.

Here Comes the Sun

Words and Music by George Harrison

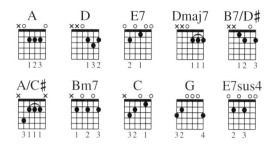

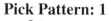

Strum Pattern: 2, 6
Pick Pattern: 1

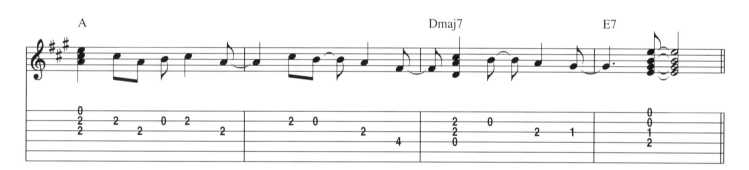

Chorus

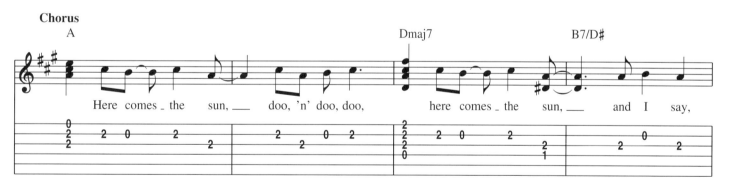

Here comes __ the sun, __ doo, 'n' doo, doo, here comes __ the sun, __ and I say,

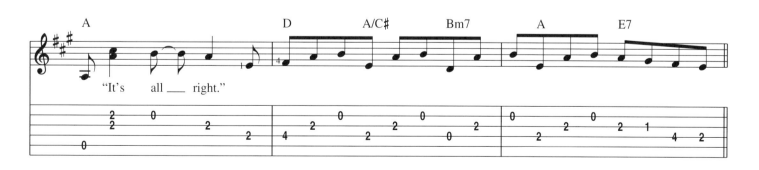

"It's all __ right."

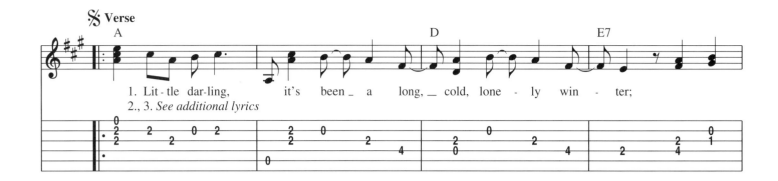

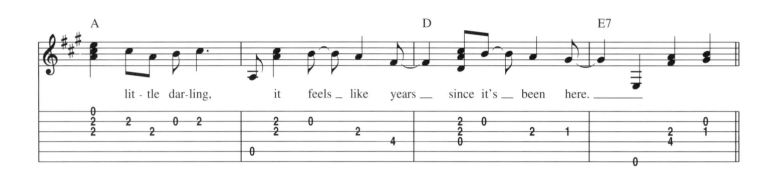

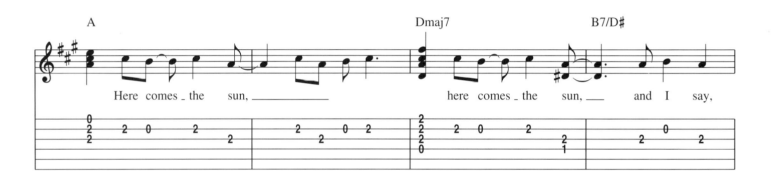

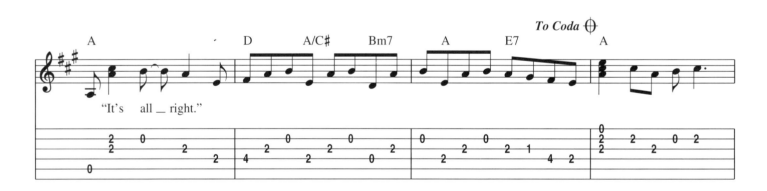

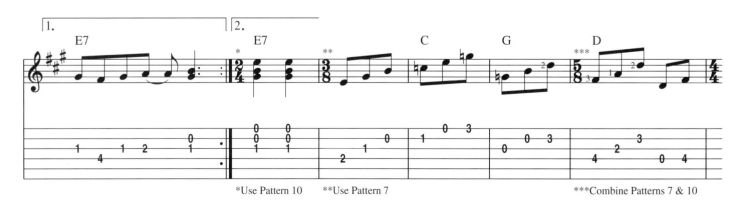

*Use Pattern 10   **Use Pattern 7   ***Combine Patterns 7 & 10

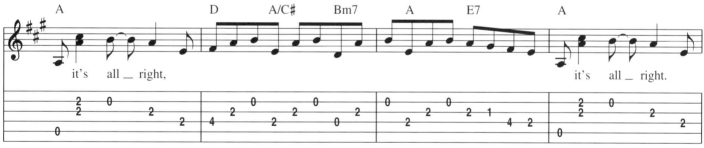

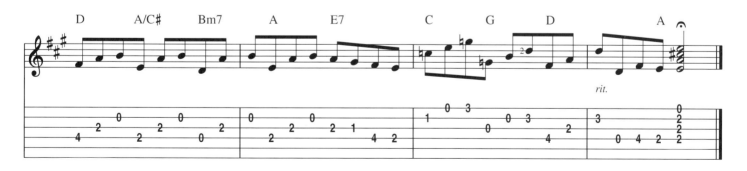

Additional Lyrics

2. Little darling,
   The smiles returning to their faces;
   Little darling,
   It seems like years since it's been here.

3. Little darling,
   I feel that ice is slowly melting;
   Little darling,
   It seems like years since it's been clear.

Georgia on My Mind

Words by Stuart Gorrell
Music by Hoagy Carmichael

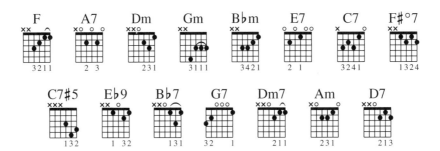

Strum Pattern: 3, 4
Pick Pattern: 3, 4

Verse
Slowly

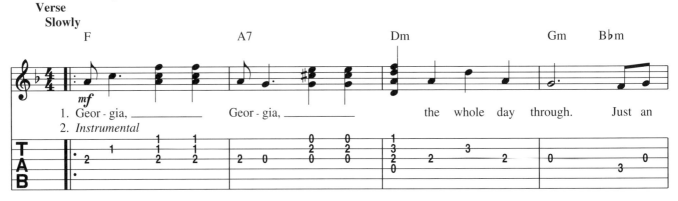

1. Geor - gia, _____ Geor - gia, _____ the whole day through. Just an
2. *Instrumental*

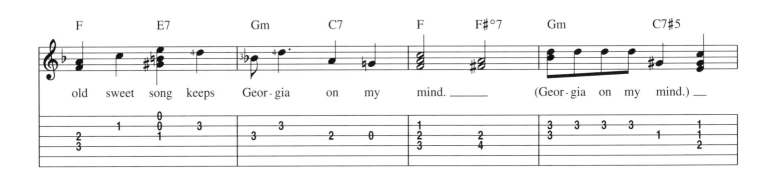

old sweet song keeps Geor - gia on my mind. _____ (Geor - gia on my mind.) _

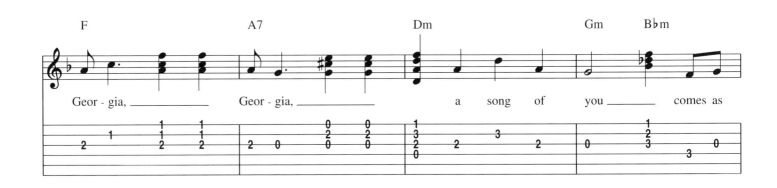

Geor - gia, _____ Geor - gia, _____ a song of you _____ comes as

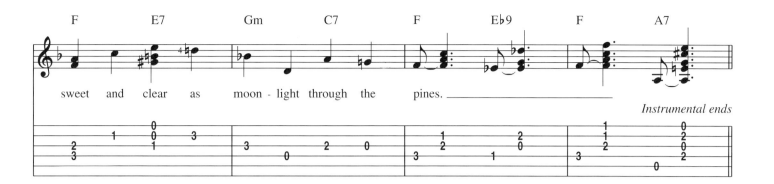

sweet and clear as moon - light through the pines. _____

Instrumental ends

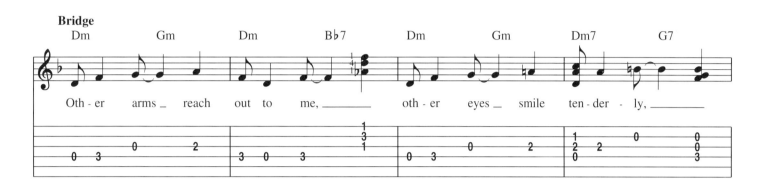

Bridge

Oth - er arms __ reach out to me, _____ oth - er eyes __ smile ten - der - ly, _____

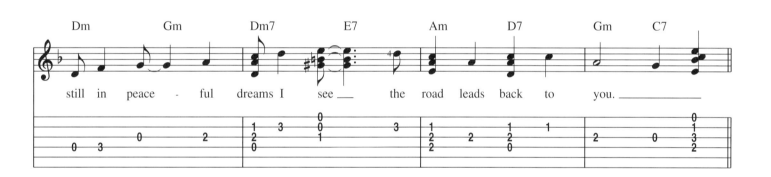

still in peace - ful dreams I see __ the road leads back to you. _____

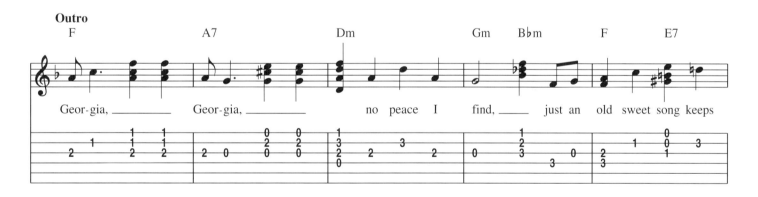

Outro

Geor-gia, _____ Geor-gia, _____ no peace I find, _____ just an old sweet song keeps

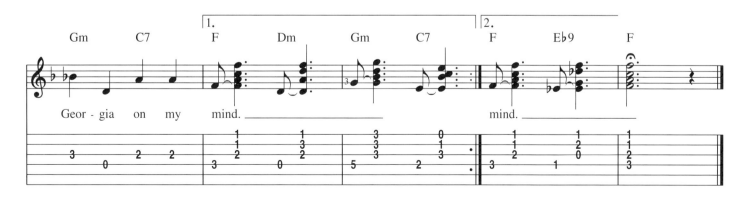

Geor - gia on my mind. _____ mind. _____

How Insensitive

(Insensatez)

Original Words by Vinicius de Moraes
English Words by Norman Gimbel
Music by Antonio Carlos Jobim

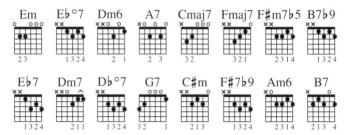

Strum Pattern: 3
Pick Pattern: 3

Verse
Medium Bossa

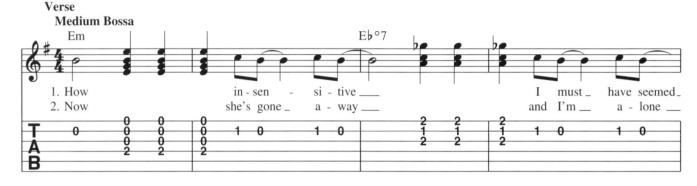

1. How in-sen-si-tive ___ I must ___ have seemed ___
2. Now she's gone ___ a-way ___ and I'm ___ a-lone ___

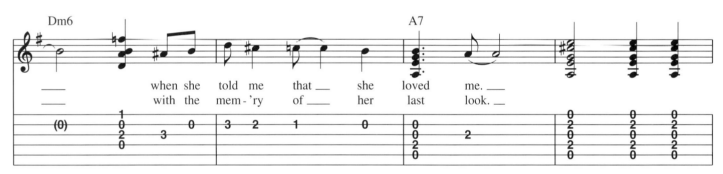

___ when she told me that ___ she loved me. ___
___ with the mem-'ry of ___ her last look. ___

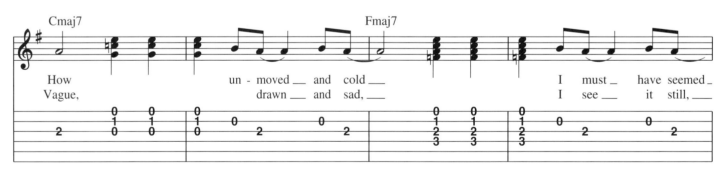

How un-moved ___ and cold ___ I must ___ have seemed ___
Vague, drawn ___ and sad, ___ I see ___ it still, ___

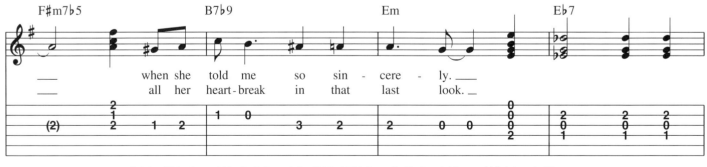

___ when she told me so sin-cere-ly. ___
___ all her heart-break in that last look. ___

I Got You
(I Feel Good)

Words and Music by James Brown

 D7   G7   A7

Strum Pattern: 2
Pick Pattern: 4

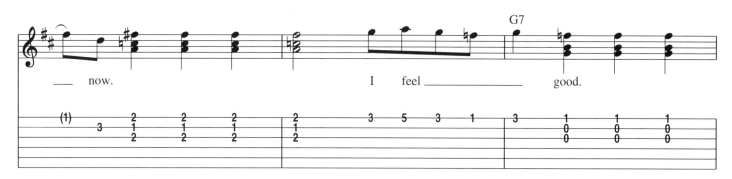

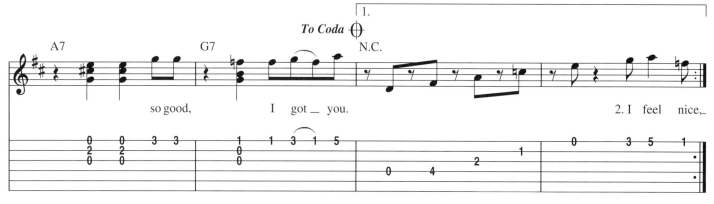

Interlude

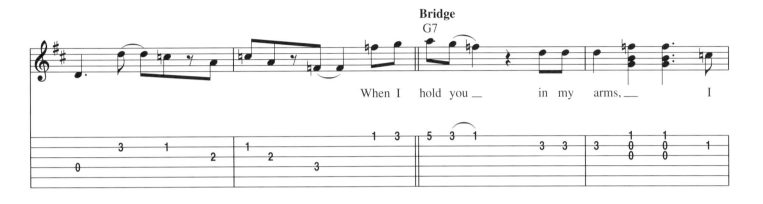

Bridge

When I hold you ___ in my arms, ___ I

know that I can do no wrong. _____ And when I hold you in ___ my arms, my

Verse

{ love won't do you no harm. ___ }
{ love can't do me no harm. ___ } 3., 4. And I feel ___ nice, ___ ah, sug-ar and spice.

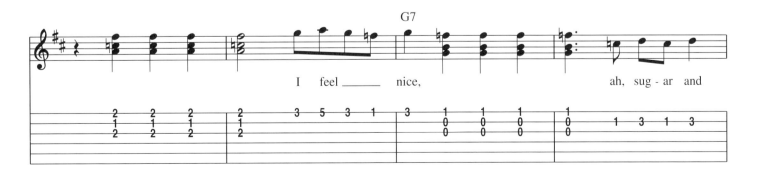

I feel ___ nice, ah, sug-ar and

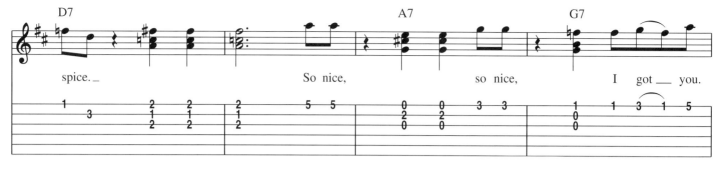

spice. _   So nice,   so nice,   I got __ you.

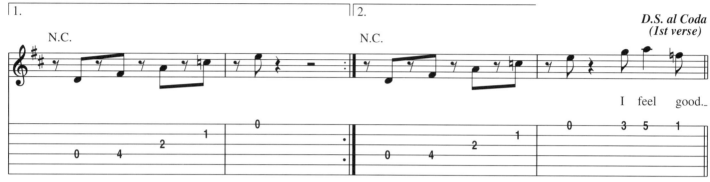

1.   **2.**   ***D.S. al Coda***
(1st verse)

I feel good. _

$\oplus$ *Coda*

So good,   so good,   'cause I got __ you.

So good,   so good,   'cause I got __ you.

rit.   Hey!

Additional Lyrics

2. I feel nice, ah, sugar and spice.
I feel nice, ah, sugar and spice.
So nice, so nice, I got you.

In My Life

Words and Music by John Lennon and Paul McCartney

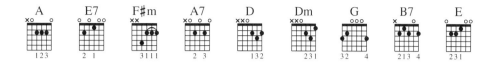

Strum Pattern: 6
Pick Pattern: 5

Intro
Moderately

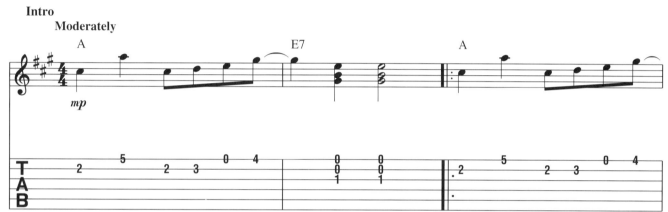

Verse

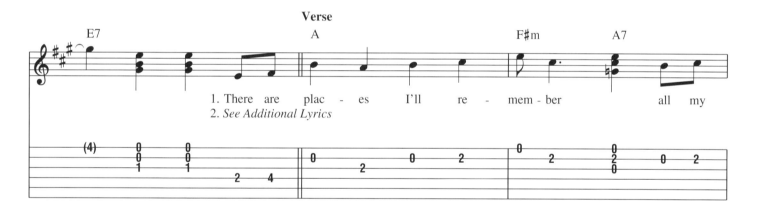

1. There are plac - es I'll re - mem - ber   all my
2. *See Additional Lyrics*

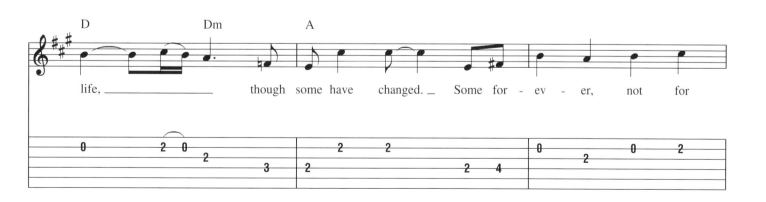

life, _____ though some have changed. _ Some for - ev - er, not for

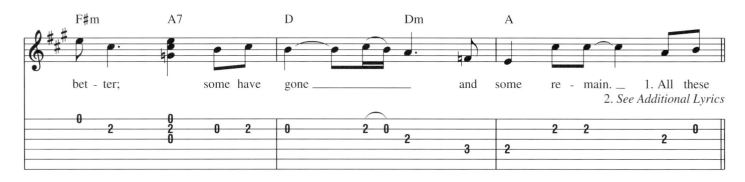

Bridge

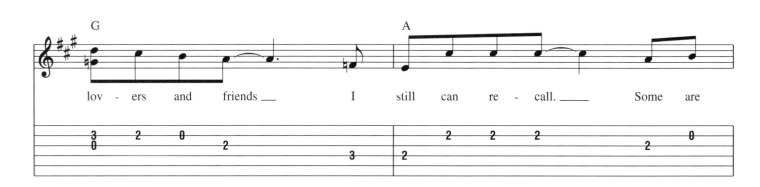

To Coda ⊕ **Interlude**

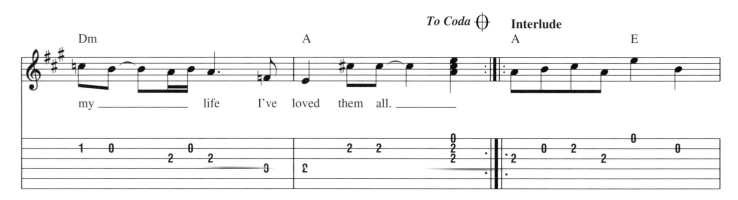

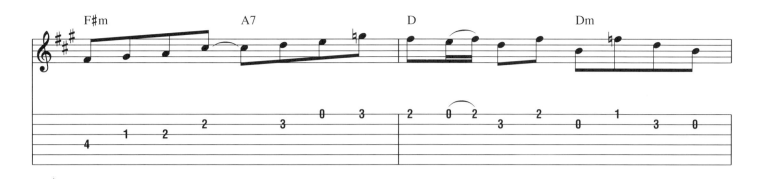

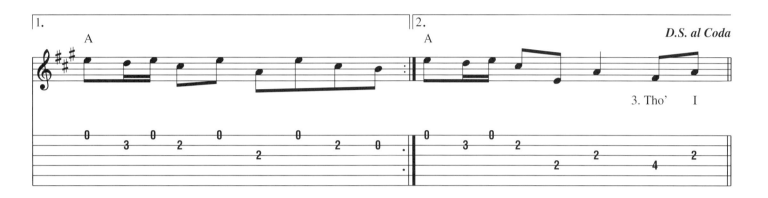

Coda

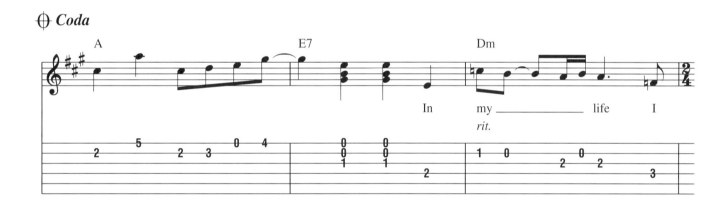

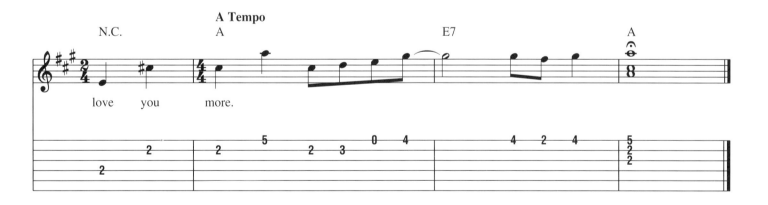

Additional Lyrics

2. But of all these friends and lovers,
   There is no one compares with you.
   And these mem'ries lose their meaning
   When I think of love as something new.

Bridge 2., 3. Tho' I know I'll never lose affection
   For people and things that went before.
   I know I'll often stop and think about them,
   In my life I'll love you more.

I Shot The Sheriff

Words and Music by Bob Marley

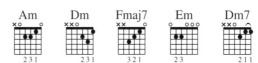

Strum Pattern: 3

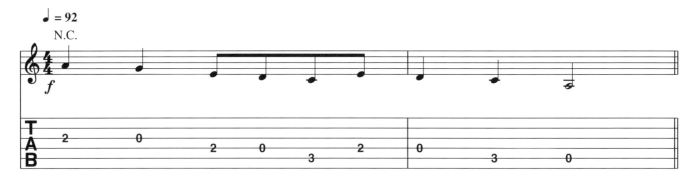

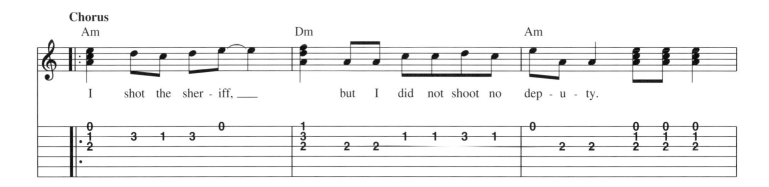

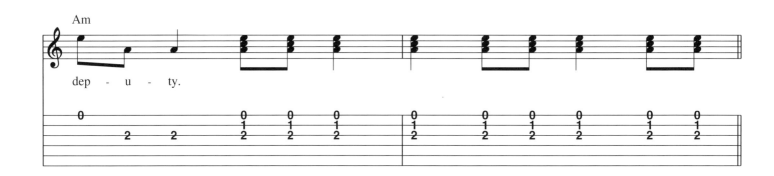

Additional Lyrics

2. Sheriff John Brown always hated me;
    For what, I don't know.
    And every time that I plant a seed,
    He said, "Kill it before it grows,"
    "Kill it before it grows."

3. Freedom came our way one day,
    So I started out of town.
    All of a sudden, I see Sheriff Brown
    Aimin' to shoot me down,
    So I shot him down.

4. Reflexes got the better of me,
    What will be will be.
    Every day, the bucket goes to the well,
    One day the bottom will drop out
    I say, one day the bottom will drop out.

I Want to Hold Your Hand

Words and Music by John Lennon and Paul McCartney

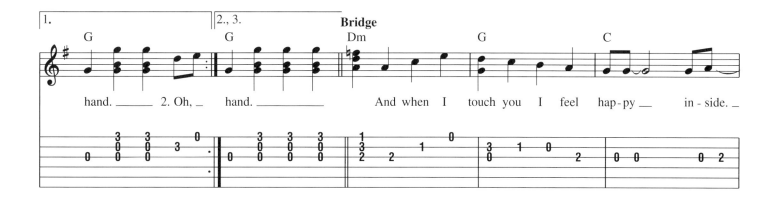

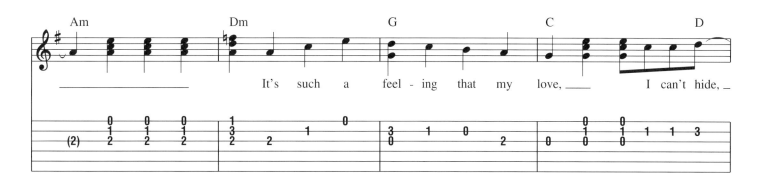

1st time, D.S.
2nd time, D.S. al Coda

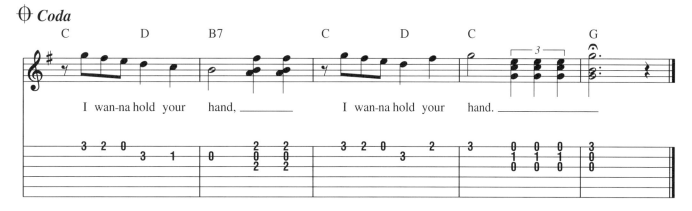

Additional Lyrics

2. Oh, please say to me
   You'll let me be your man.
   And please say to me
   You'll let me hold your hand.

3. Yeah, you got that somethin',
   I think you'll understand.
   When I { say / feel } that something,
   I wanna hold your hand.

I'm Your Hoochie Coochie Man

Written by Willie Dixon

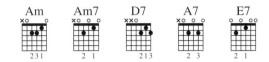

Strum Pattern: **8**
Pick Pattern: **8**

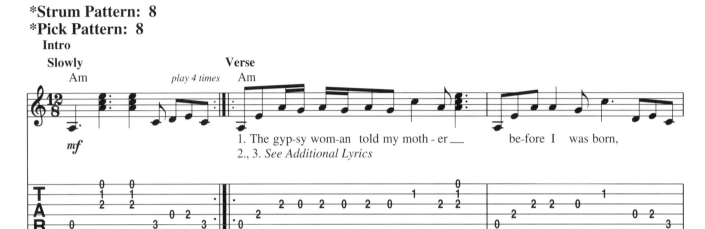

*Play patterns 4 times per measure.

"You got a boy - child com - ing, ___ gon-na be a son - of - a gun.

Gon - na make pret - ty wom - en, ___ gon-na make 'em jump and shout."

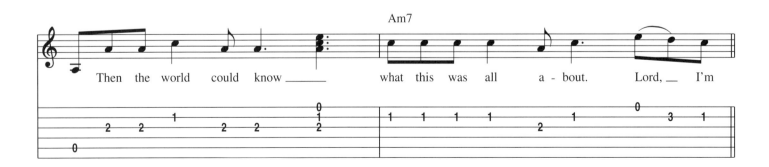

Then the world could know _____ what this was all a - bout. Lord, ___ I'm

Additional Lyrics

2. I got a black cat's bone,
   I got a mojo too.
   I'm John the Conqueror,
   I'm gonna mess with you.
   Gonna make you pretty girls
   Lead me by the hand.
   Then the world will know
   I'm the hoochie coohie man.

3. On the seventh hour,
   And on the seventh day,
   On the seventh month,
   The seven doctors say,
   "He was born for good luck
   And that you're gonna see."
   I've got seven hundred dollars, baby,
   Don't you mess with me.

If I Ever Lose My Faith in You

Written and Composed by Sting

Strum Pattern: 6
Pick Pattern: 2

Intro
Moderately

% Verse

1.You could say I lost my faith in sci - ence and pro - gress.
2., 3. *See Additional Lyrics*

You could say I lost my be - lief in the ho - ly ____ church.

You could say I lost my sense of di - rec -

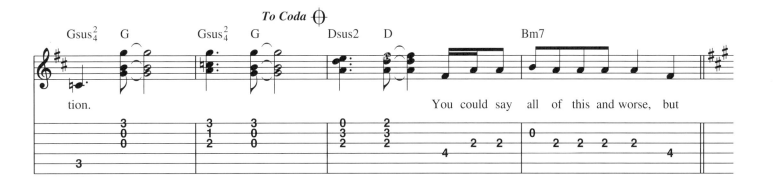

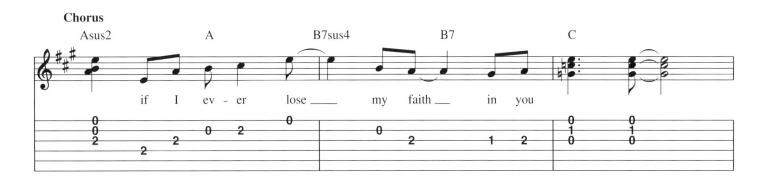

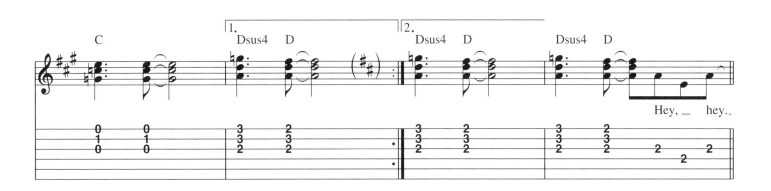

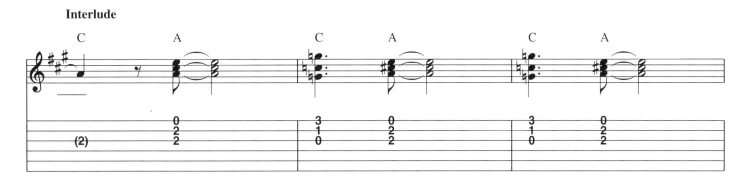

Bridge

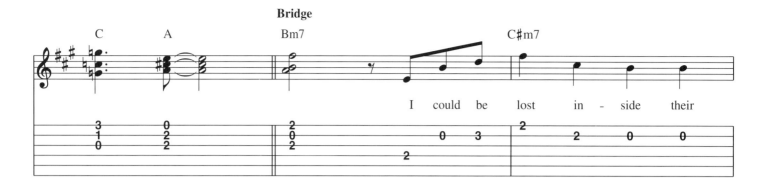

I could be lost in - side their

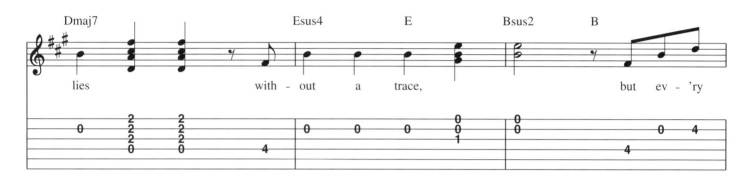

lies with - out a trace, but ev - 'ry

D.S. al Coda

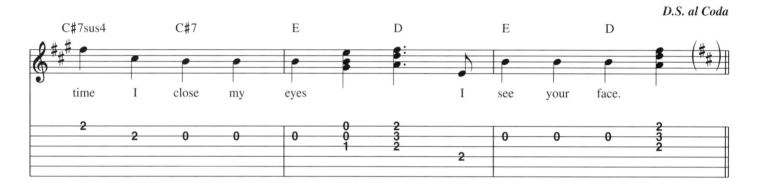

time I close my eyes I see your face.

⊕ *Coda*

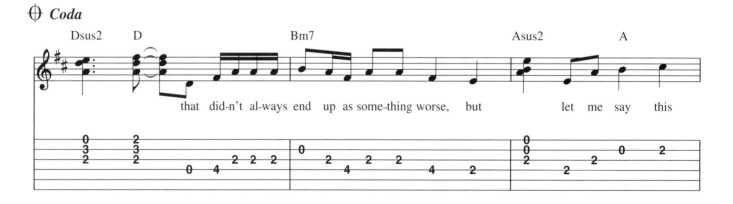

that did-n't al-ways end up as some-thing worse, but let me say this

Chorus

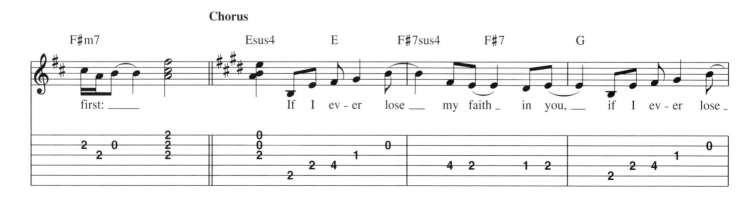

first: _____ If I ev - er lose ___ my faith _ in you, ___ if I ev - er lose _

Chorus

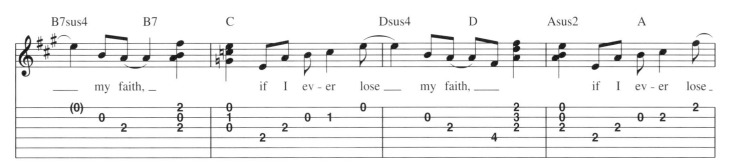

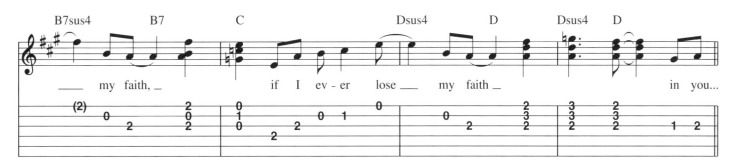

Outro

Repeat and Fade

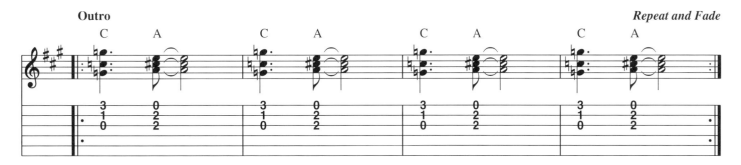

Additional Lyrics

2. Some would say I was a lost man in a lost world.
   You could say I lost my faith in the people on TV.
   You could say I lost my belief in our politicians.
   They all seem like game show hosts to me.

3. I never saw no miracle of science
   That didn't go from a blessing to a curse.
   I never saw no military solution
   That didn't always end up as something worse,
   But let me say this first:

Imagine

Words and Music by John Lennon

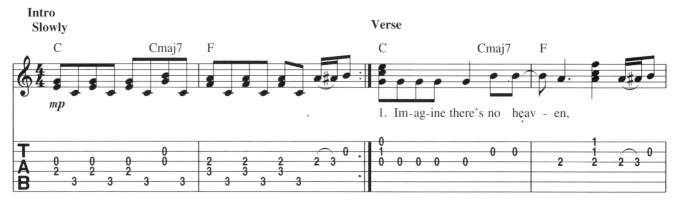

Strum Pattern: 1
Pick Pattern: 2

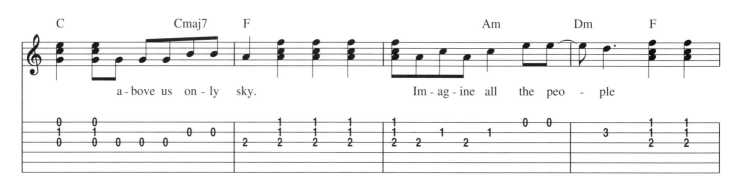

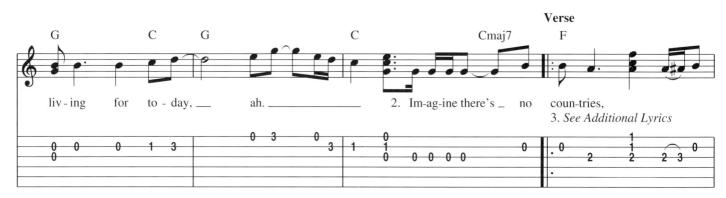

Additional Lyrics

3. Imagine no possessions,
   I wonder if you can;
   No need for greed or hunger,
   A brotherhood of man.
   Imagine all the people sharing all the world.

Invisible Touch

Words and Music by Tony Banks, Phil Collins and Mike Rutherford

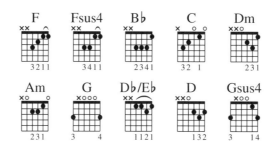

Strum Pattern: 4
Pick Pattern: 1

1. Well, I've been wait-ing,
2., 3. *See additional lyrics*

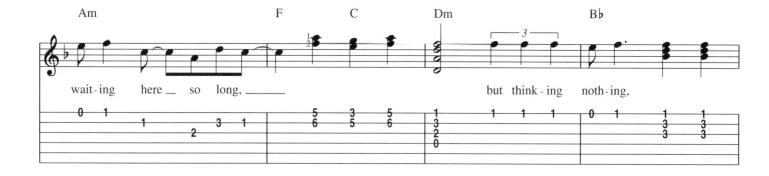

wait-ing here __ so long, _____ but think-ing noth-ing,

noth-ing could __ go wrong. _____ But now I know __ she has a

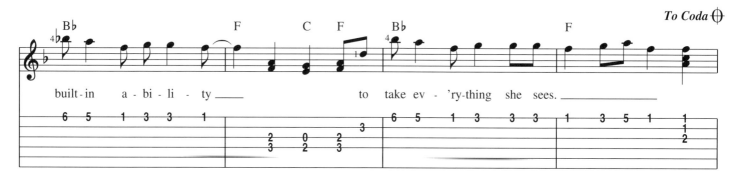

built-in a-bil-i-ty _____ to take ev-'ry-thing she sees. _____

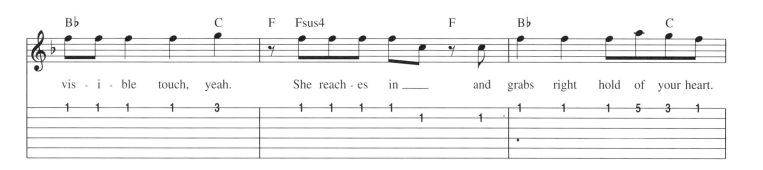

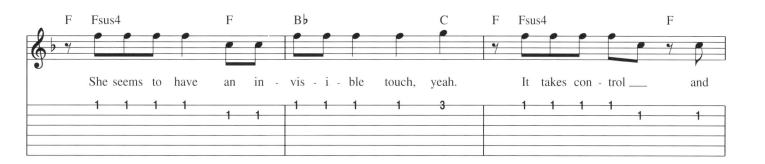

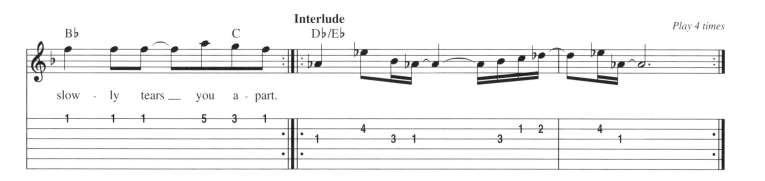

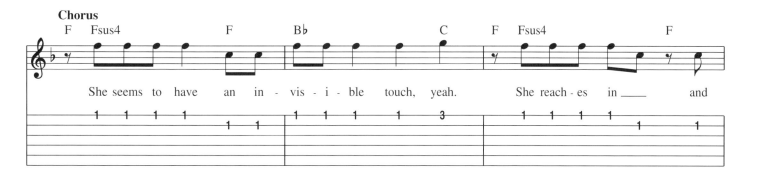

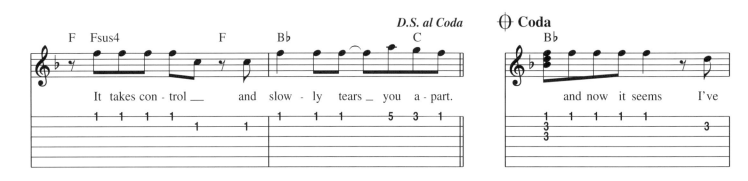

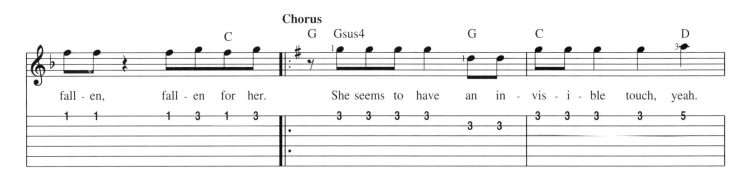

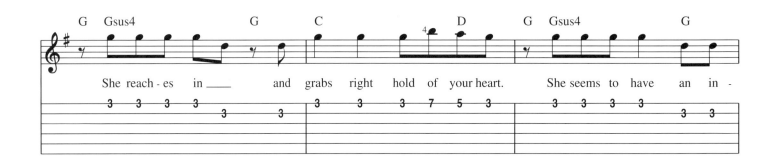

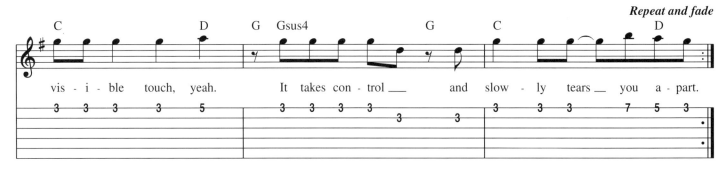

Additional Lyrics

2. I don't really know her; I only know her name.
   But she crawls under your skin; you're never quite the same.
   And now I know she's got something you just can't trust,
   Something mysterious.
   And now it seems I'm falling, falling for her.

3. She don't like losing; to her it's still a game.
   And though she will mess up your life, you'll want her just the same.
   And now I know she has a built-in ability
   To take everything she sees.
   And now it seems I've fallen, fallen for her.

Killing Floor

By Chester Burnett

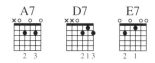

Strum Pattern: 1
Pick Pattern: 2

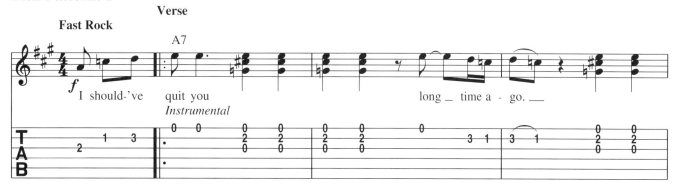

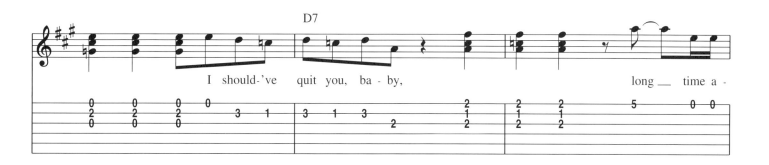

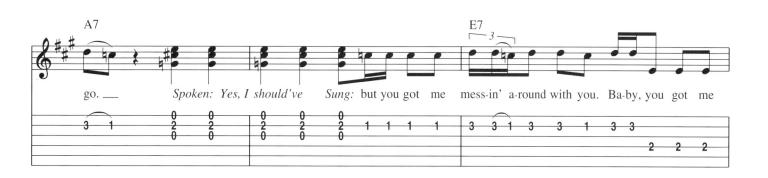

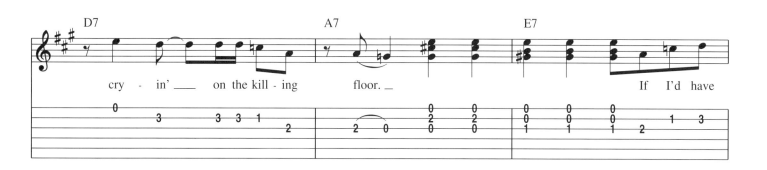

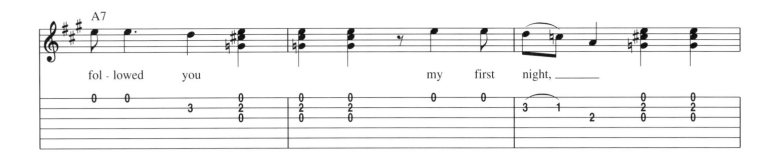

fol - lowed you   my first   night, _____

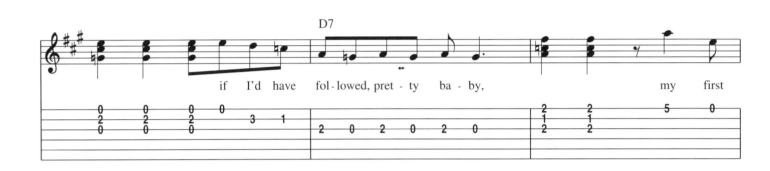

if   I'd   have   fol - lowed, pret - ty   ba - by,   my   first

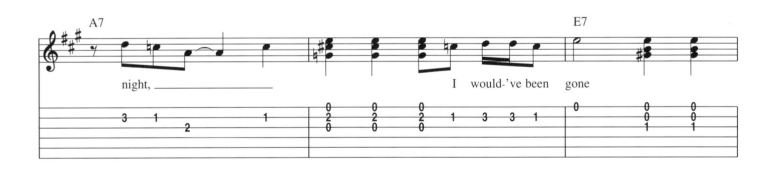

night, _____   I   would-'ve   been   gone

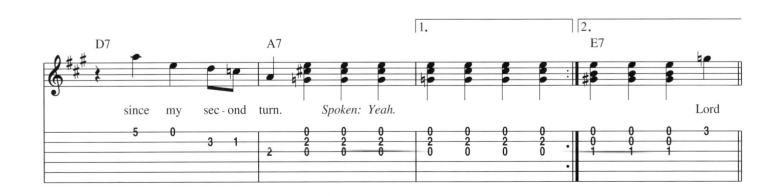

since   my   sec - ond   turn.   *Spoken: Yeah.*   Lord

Outro

knows, _ Lord knows _ I should-'ve been gone.
Spoken: You got me hot.

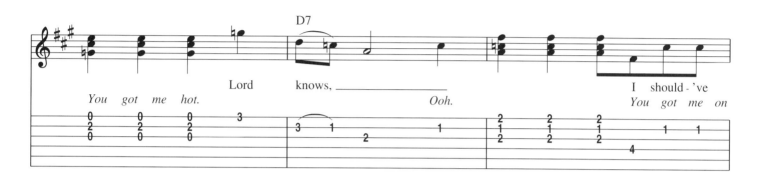

Lord knows, _____ Ooh. I should -'ve
You got me hot. *You got me on*

been gone. She got me mess-in' a-round with you, ba-by, you got me
you, babe. Ooh.

1.

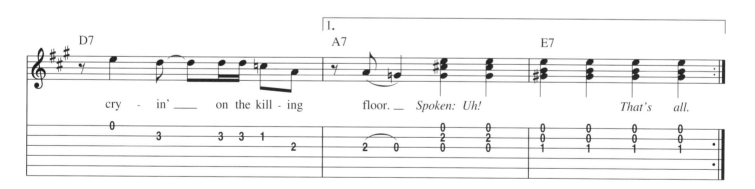

cry - in' ____ on the kill - ing floor. _ *Spoken: Uh!* That's all.

2.

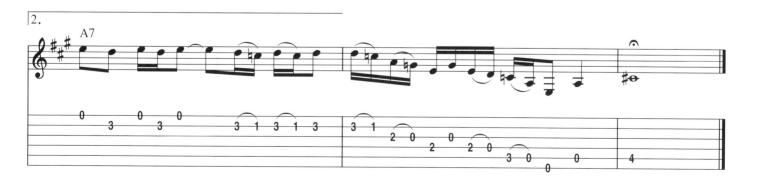

Jambalaya
(On the Bayou)

Words and Music by Hank Williams

Strum Pattern: 4
Pick Pattern: 1

Verse

Moderately

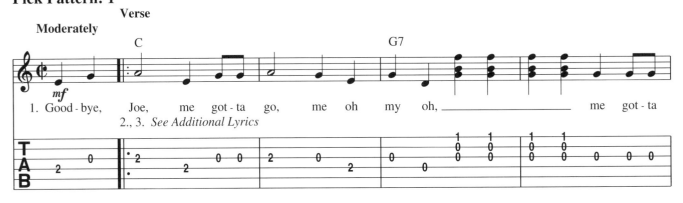

1. Good - bye, Joe, me got - ta go, me oh my oh, _____ me got - ta
2., 3. *See Additional Lyrics*

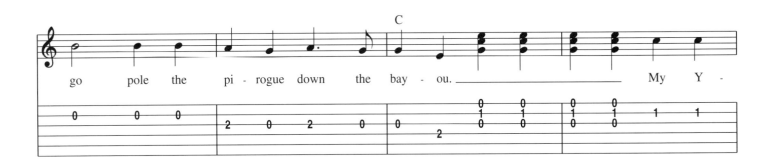

go pole the pi - rogue down the bay - ou. _____ My Y -

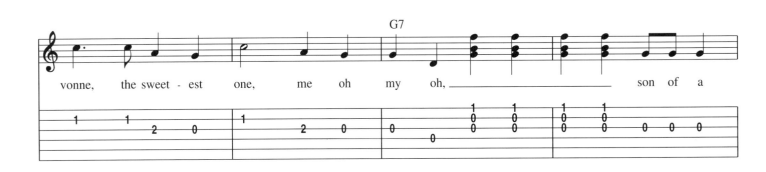

vonne, the sweet - est one, me oh my oh, _____ son of a

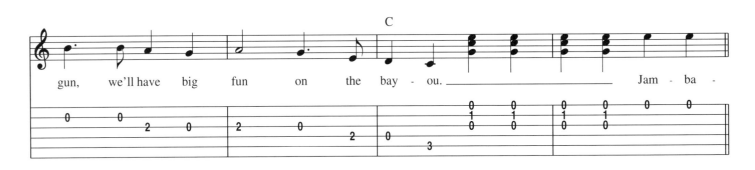

gun, we'll have big fun on the bay - ou. _____ Jam - ba -

Chorus

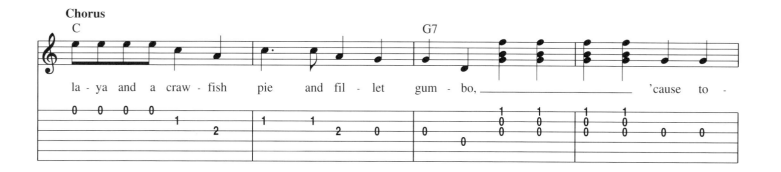

la - ya and a craw - fish pie and fil - let gum - bo, _____ 'cause to -

night I'm gon - na see my ma cher a - mi - o. _____ Pick gui -

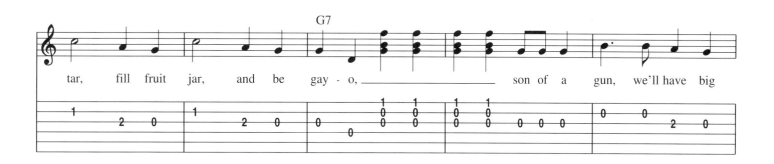

tar, fill fruit jar, and be gay - o, _____ son of a gun, we'll have big

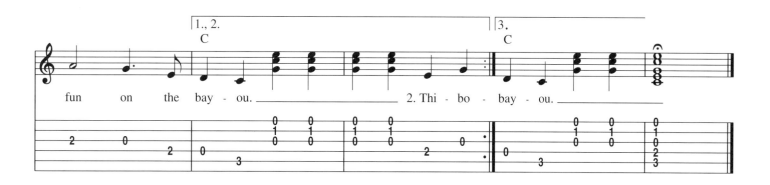

fun on the bay - ou. _____ 2. Thi - bo - bay - ou. _____

Additional Lyrics

2. Thibodaux, Fontaineaux, the place is buzzin',
   Kin folk come to see Yvonne by the dozen.
   Dress in style and go hog wild, me oh my oh,
   Son of a gun, we'll have big fun on the bayou.

3. Settle down far from town, get me a pirogue,
   And I'll catch all the fish in the bayou.
   Swap my mon to buy Yvonne what we need-o,
   Son of a gun, we'll have big fun on the bayou.

Johnny B. Goode

Words and Music by Chuck Berry

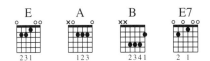

Strum Pattern: 1, 6
Pick Pattern: 4, 5

Intro
Bright Rock Beat

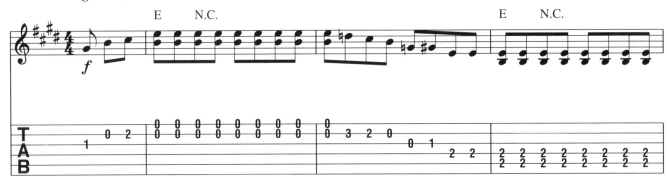

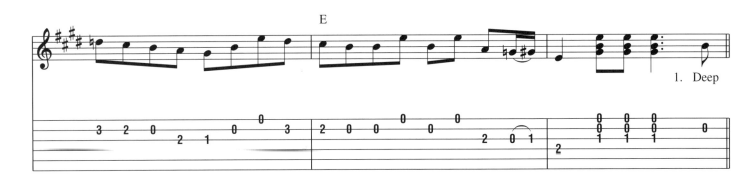

%: **Verse**

down in Lou - 'si - an - a, close to New Or - leans, ___ way
2., 3. *See Additional Lyrics*

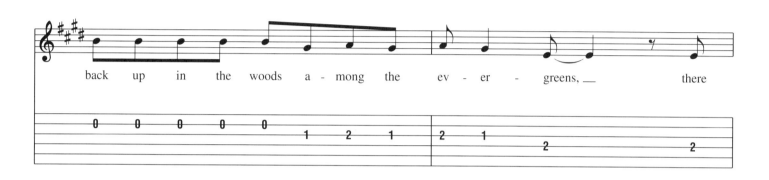

back up in the woods a - mong the ev - er - greens, ___ there

stood a log cab - in made of earth and wood _ where lived a coun - try boy named _

John - ny B. Goode, _ who nev - er, ev - er learned to read or

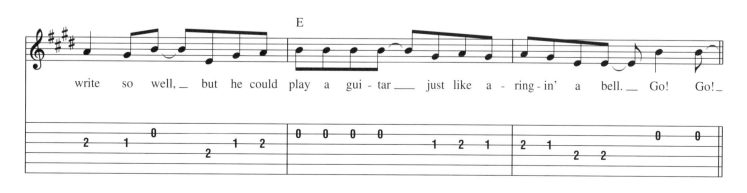

write so well, _ but he could play a gui - tar ___ just like a - ring - in' a bell. _ Go! Go!_

Chorus

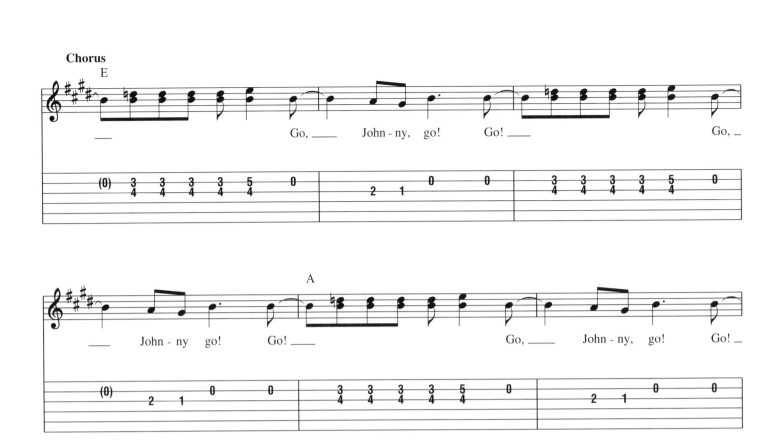

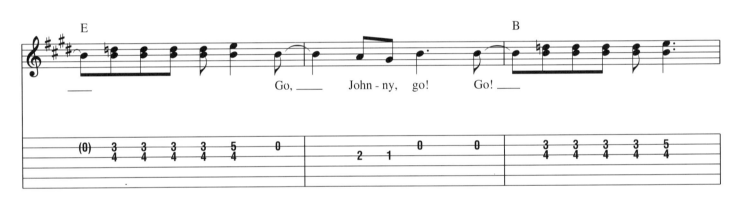

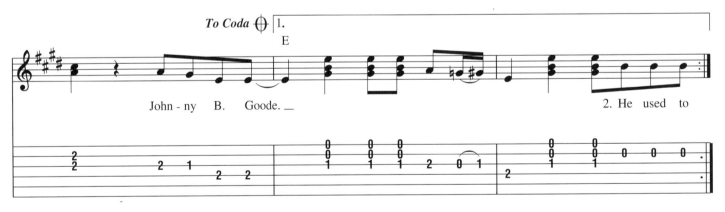

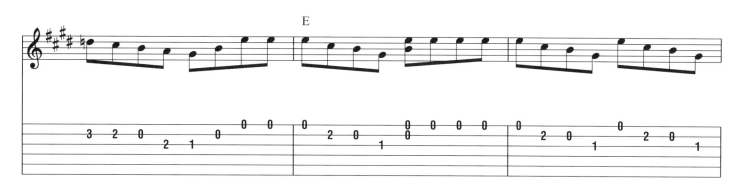

D.S. al Coda

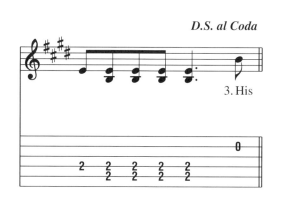

3. His

✛ *Coda*

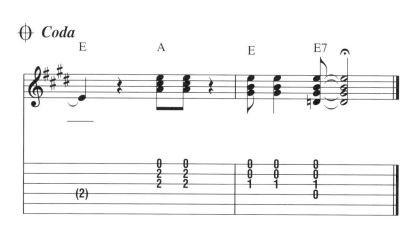

Additional Lyrics

2. He used to carry his guitar in a gunny sack,
Go sit beneath the tree by the railroad track.
Old engineers would see him sittin' in the shade,
Strummin' with the rhythm that the drivers made.
When people passed by him they would stop and say,
"Oh my, but that little country boy could play."

3. His mother told him, "Someday you will be a man,
And you will be the leader of a big ol' band.
Many people comin' from miles around
Will hear you play your music when the sun go down.
Maybe some day your name will be in lights,
Sayin', "Johnny B. Goode tonight."

Let It Be

Words and Music by John Lennon and Paul McCartney

Intro
Moderately Slow

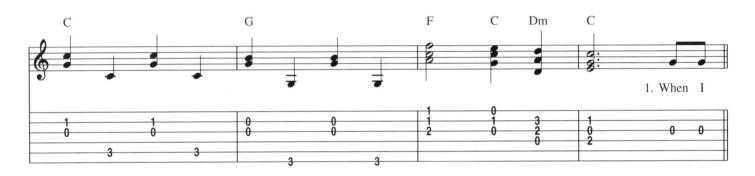

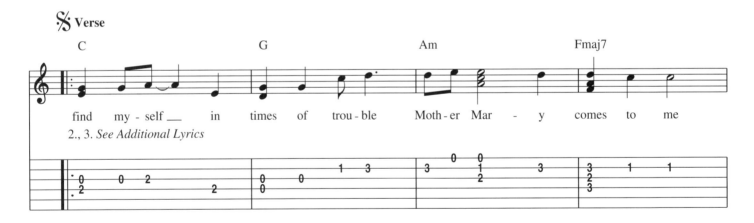

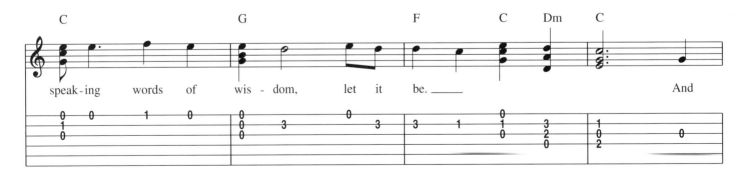

2., 3. See Additional Lyrics

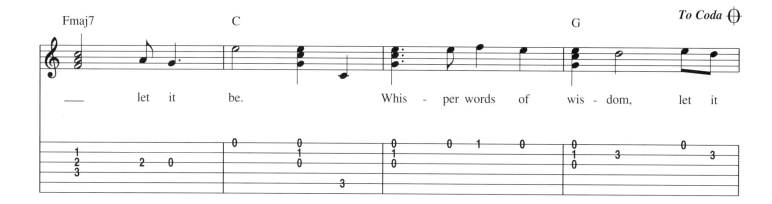

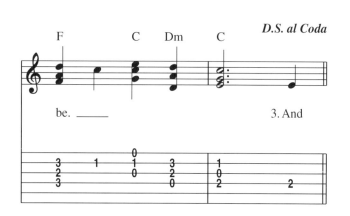

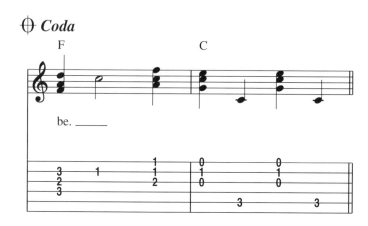

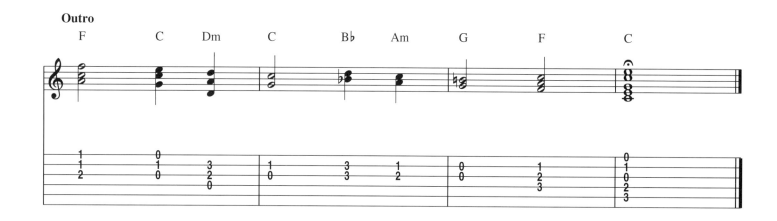

Additional Lyrics

2. And when the broken hearted people
   Living in the world agree,
   There will be an answer, let it be.
   For tho' they may be parted
   There is still a chance that they will see.
   There will be an answer, let it be.

3. And when the night is cloudy
   There is still a light that shines on me.
   Shine until tomorrow, let it be.
   I wake up to the sound of music
   Mother Mary comes to me
   Speaking words of wisdom, let it be.

Light My Fire

Words and Music by The Doors

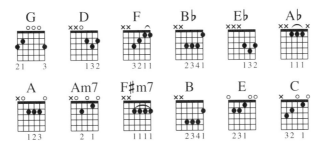

Strum Pattern: 1, 6
Pick Pattern: 2, 6

Intro
Moderate Rock

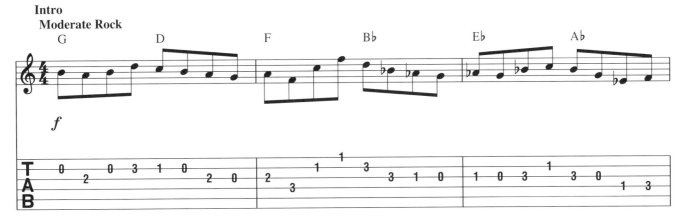

Verse

1. You know that it would be un-true. ____ You
2. *See Additional Lyrics*

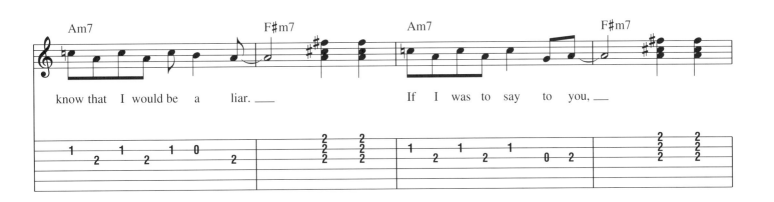

know that I would be a liar. ____ If I was to say to you, ____

girl, we could-n't get much higher. ___ Come on, ba-by, light my fire. ___

Come on, ba-by, light my fire. ___ Try to set the night on

fire. 2. The 3. The time to hes-i-tate is through. _

No time to wal-low in the mire. ___ Try now we can on-ly lose. _

And our love be-come a fun'-ral pyre. _____

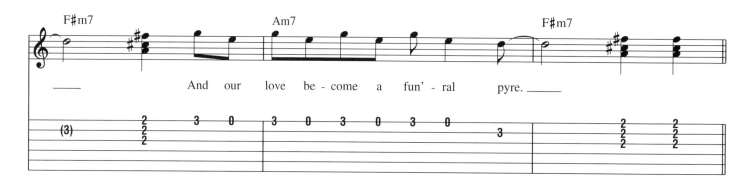

Additional Lyrics

2. The time to hesitate is through,
   No time to wallow in the mire.
   Try now we can only lose,
   And our love become a funeral pyre.

Low Rider

Words and Music by Sylvester Allen, Harold R. Brown, Morris Dickerson,
Jerry Goldstein, Leroy Jordan, Lee Oskar, Charles W. Miller and Howard Scott

Strum Pattern: 4
Pick Pattern: 1, 4

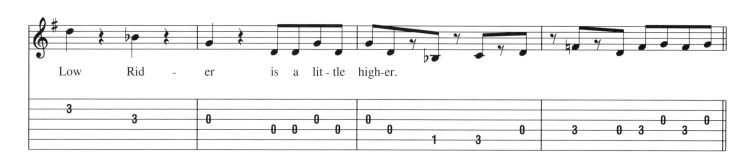

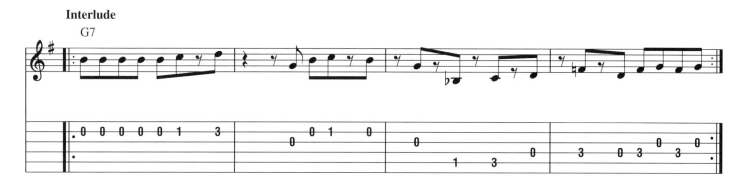

play 4 times

Bridge

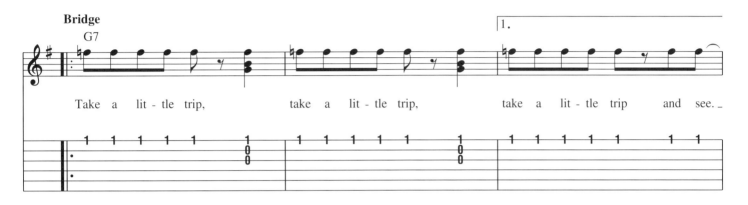

Take a lit-tle trip, take a lit-tle trip, take a lit-tle trip and see.

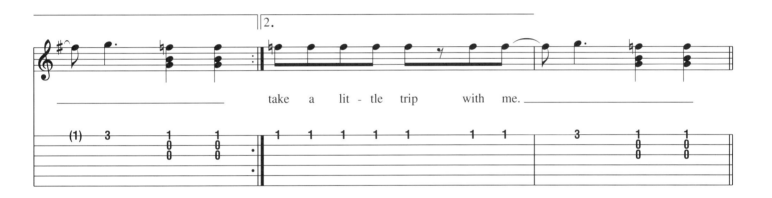

take a lit-tle trip with me.

Outro

Repeat and Fade

Additional Lyrics

2. Low Rider drives a little slower.
   Low Rider, he's a real goer.

3. Low Rider knows every street, yeah.
   Low Rider is the one to meet, yeah.

4. Low Rider don't use no gas, now.
   Low Rider don't drive too fast.

Mission: Impossible Theme

from the Paramount Television Series MISSION:IMPOSSIBLE
By Lalo Schifrin

*Strum Pattern: 8&10

*Pick Pattern: 8&10

The Rainbow Connection

from THE MUPPET MOVIE
Words and Music by Paul Williams and Kenneth L. Ascher

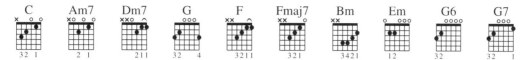

Strum Pattern: 8, 9
Pick Pattern: 8, 9

Verse
Moderately

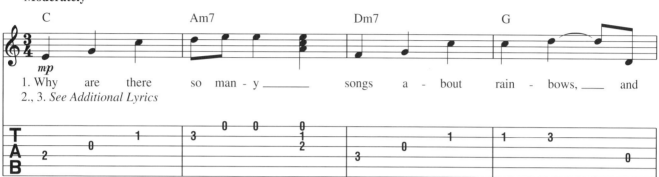

1. Why are there so man - y _____ songs a - bout rain - bows, ____ and
2., 3. *See Additional Lyrics*

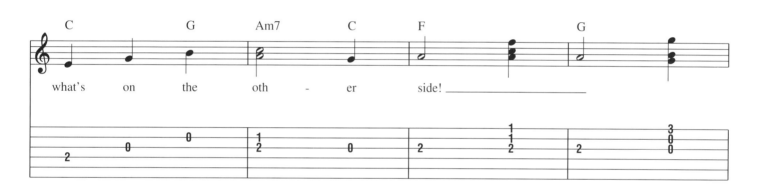

what's on the oth - er side! _____

Rain - bows are vis - ions, ____ but on - ly il - lu - sions, ____ and

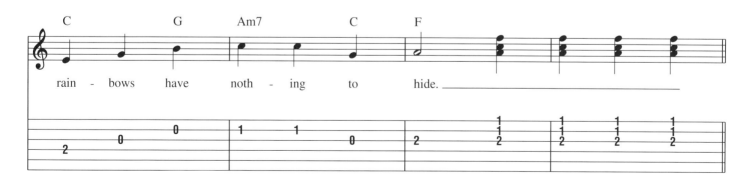

rain - bows have noth - ing to hide. _____

Chorus

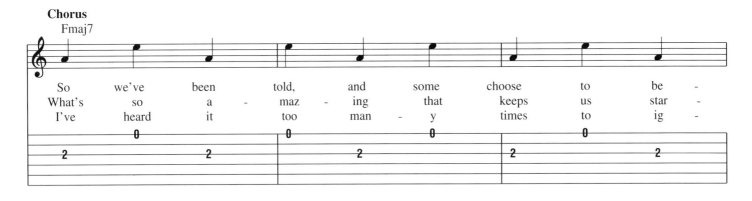

So we've been told, and some choose to be-
What's so a - maz - ing that keeps us star -
I've heard it too man - y times to ig -

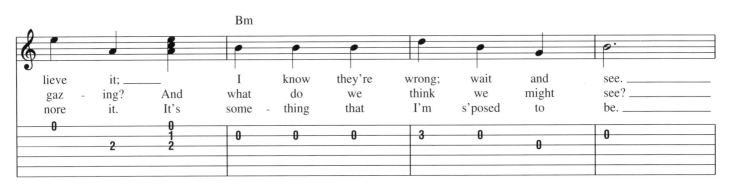

lieve it; _____ I know they're wrong; wait and see. _____
gaz - ing? And what do we think we might see? _____
nore it. It's some - thing that I'm s'posed to be. _____

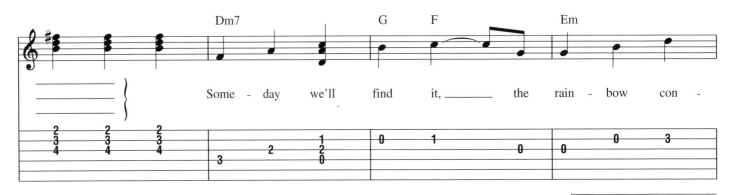

Some - day we'll find it, _____ the rain - bow con -

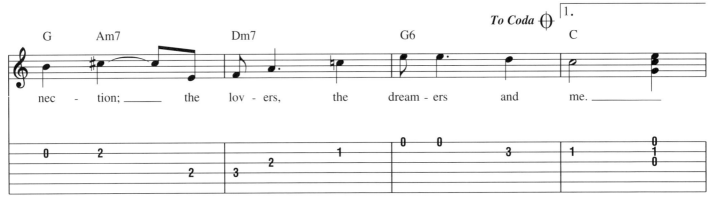

nec - tion; _____ the lov - ers, the dream - ers and me. _____

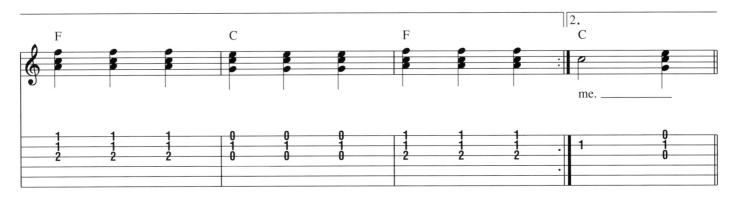

me. _____

114

Bridge

All of us un - der its spell; we know that it's

D.C. al Coda

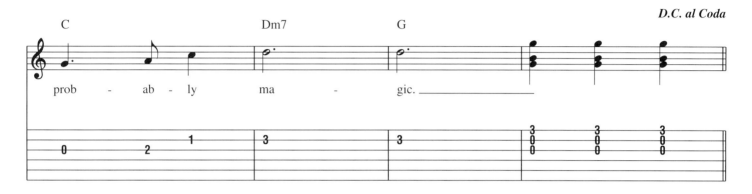

prob - ab - ly ma - gic.

Coda

Outro

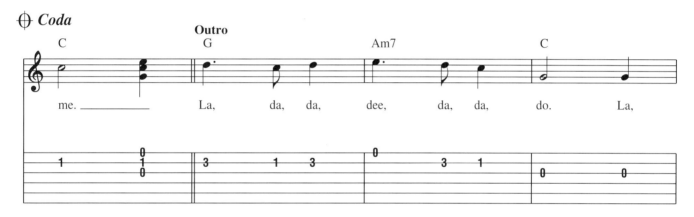

me. La, da, da, dee, da, da, do. La,

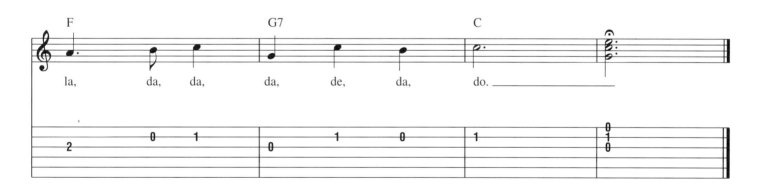

la, da, da, da, de, da, do.

Additional Lyrics

2. Who said that ev'ry wish could be heard and answered
   When wished on the morning star?
   Somebody thought of that, and someone believed it;
   Look what it's done so far.

3. Have you been half asleep and then you heard voices?
   I've heard them calling my name.
   Is this the sweet sound that calls the young sailors?
   The voice might be one and the same.

No Particular Place to Go

Words and Music by Chuck Berry

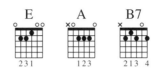

Strum Pattern: 1
Pick Pattern: 2

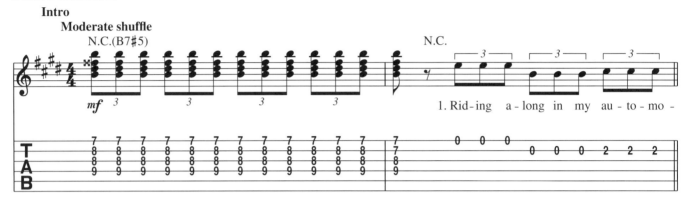

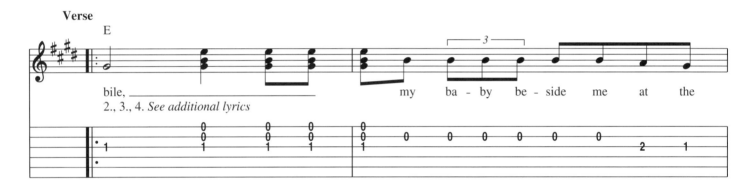

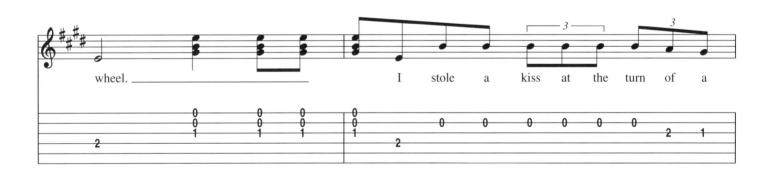

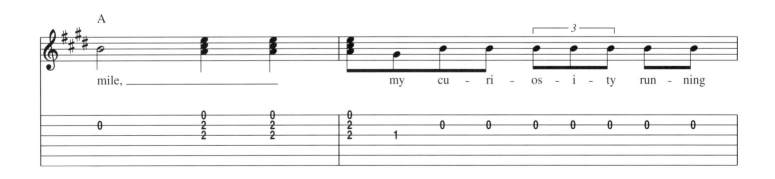

Additional Lyrics

2. Riding along in my automobile,
   I was anxious to tell her the way I feel.
   So I told her softly and sincere
   And she leaned and whispered in my ear.
   Cuddling more and driving slow,
   With no particular place to go.

3. No particular place to go,
   So we parked way out on the cocamo.
   The night was young and the moon was gold,
   So we both decided to take a stroll.
   Can you image the way I felt?
   I couldn't unfasten her safety belt.

4. Riding along in my calaboose,
   Still trying to get her belt unloose.
   All the way home I held a grudge,
   For the safety belt that wouldn't budge.
   Cruising and playing the radio,
   With no particular place to go.

Rock And Roll All Nite

Words and Music by Paul Stanley and Gene Simmons

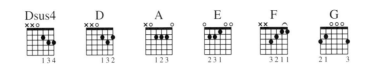

Strum Pattern: 2
Pick Pattern: 4

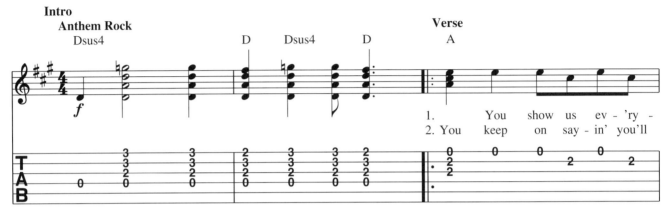

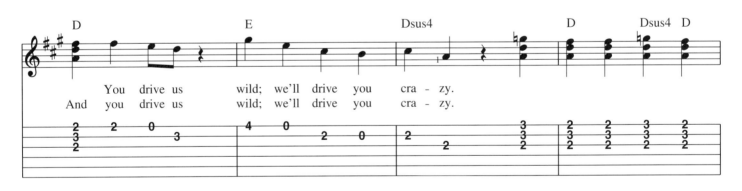

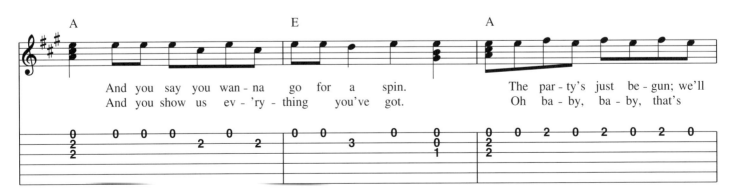

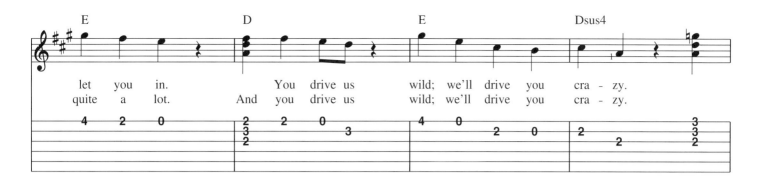

let you in.   You drive us   wild; we'll drive you   cra - zy.
quite a lot.   And you drive us   wild; we'll drive you   cra - zy.

Pre-Chorus

You keep on shout - in',   you keep on shout - in'.

Chorus

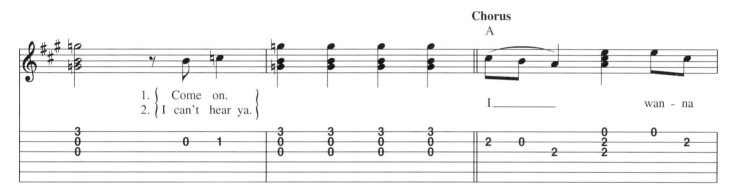

1. { Come on.
2. { I can't hear ya. }

I_____   wan - na

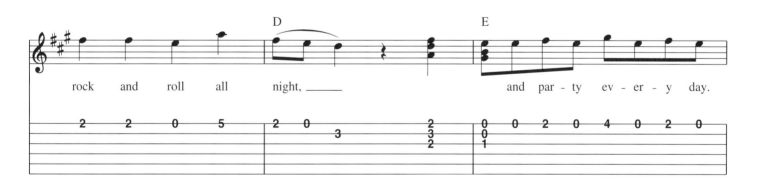

rock and roll all   night, _____   and par - ty ev - er - y day.

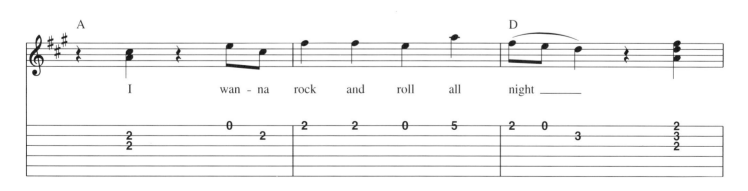

I   wan - na rock and roll all   night _____

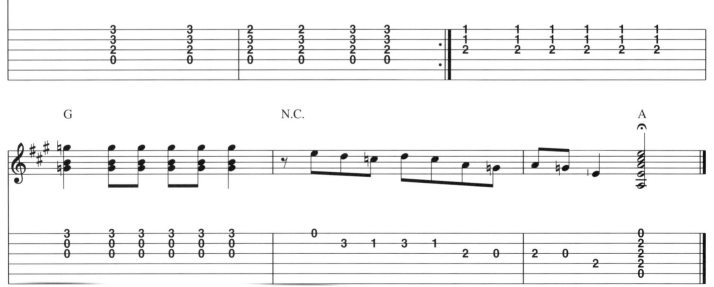

Rock and Roll Hoochie Koo

Words and Music by Rick Derringer

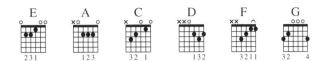

Strum Pattern: 2
Pick Pattern: 4

Intro
Moderate Rock

Verse

1. I could-n't stop mov-ing when it first took hold. _____
2., 3. *See Additional Lyrics*

It was a warm spring night at the old town hall.

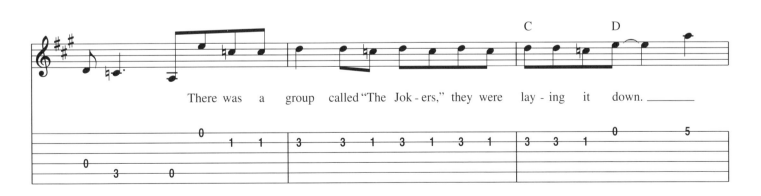

There was a group called "The Jok-ers," they were lay-ing it down. _____

But you know I'm nev - er gon - na lose that

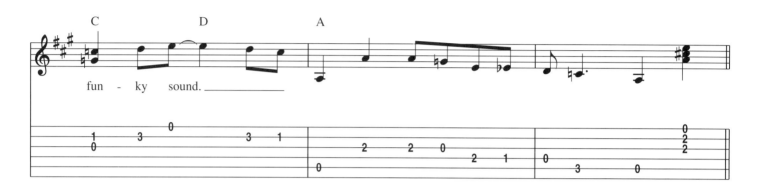

fun - ky sound. _____

Chorus

Rock and roll _____ hoo - chie koo. _____

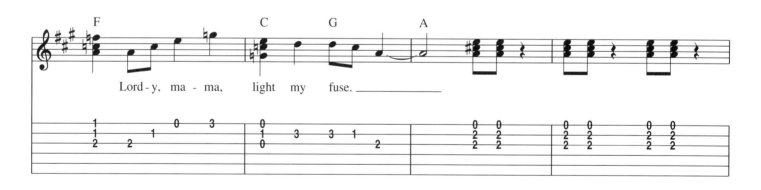

Lord - y, ma - ma, light my fuse. _____

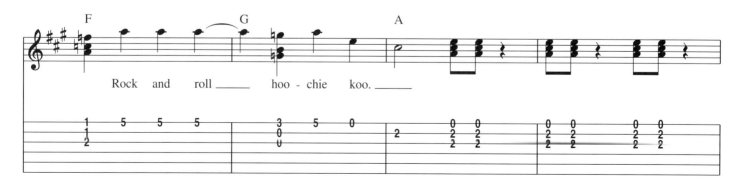

Rock and roll _____ hoo - chie koo. _____

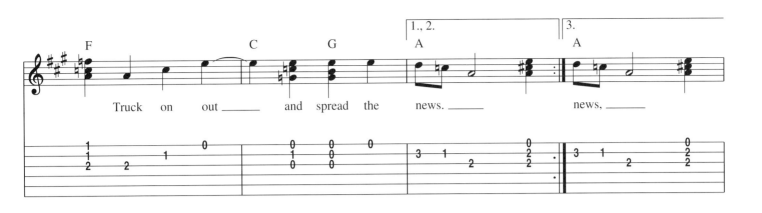

Truck on out _____ and spread the news. _____ news, _____

yeah, that I'm tired _____ of pay - in' dues. _____

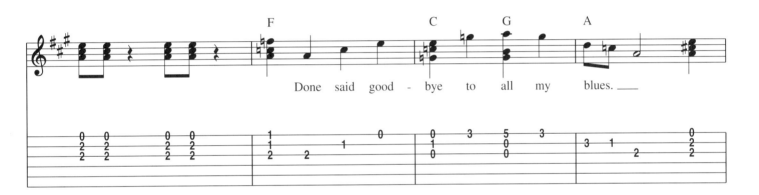

Done said good - bye to all my blues. _____

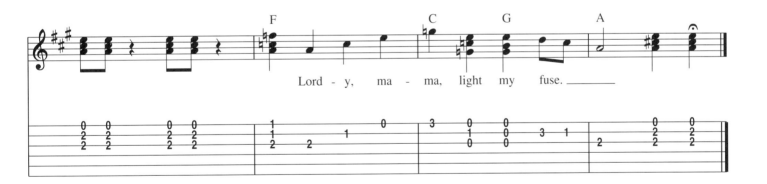

Lord - y, ma - ma, light my fuse. _____

Additional Lyrics

2. Mosquitos started buzzing 'bout this time of year.
   Going out back, she said she'll meet me there.
   We were rolling in the grass that grows behind the barn.
   You know, my ears started ringing like a fire alarm.

3. I hope you all know what I'm talkin' about.
   The way they wiggle that thing really knocks me out.
   Gettin' higher all the time, hope you all are too.
   C'mon a little closer gonna do it to you.

Rock Me Baby

Words and Music by B.B. King and Joe Bihari

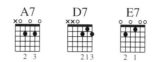

Strum Pattern: 1, 2
Pick Pattern: 2, 4

Intro
Slowly

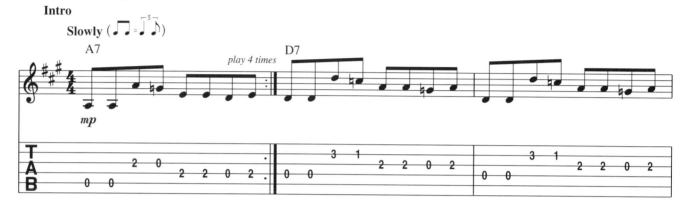

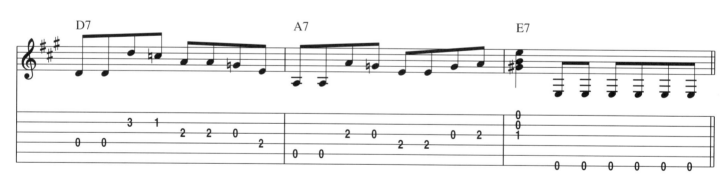

Verse

1. Rock me, ba-by, rock me all ___ night long. ___
2., 3. *See Additional Lyrics*

Rock me, ba - by, hon - ey, rock me all night

long. ___ Want you to rock me, ba - by,

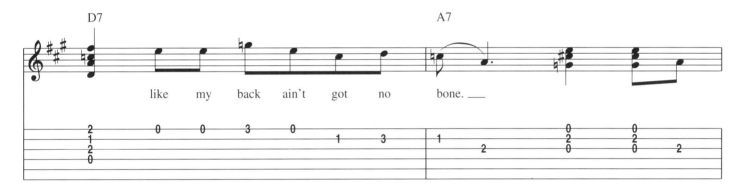

like my back ain't got no bone. ___

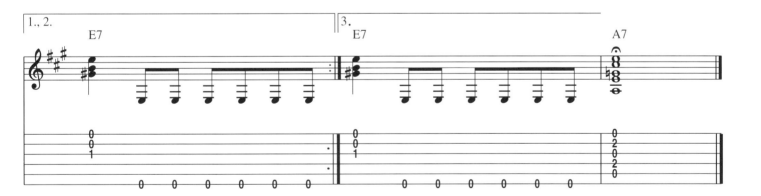

Additional Lyrics

2. Roll me, baby, like you roll a wagon wheel.
   Want you to roll me, baby, like you roll a wagon wheel.
   Want you to roll me, baby, you don't know how it makes me feel.

3. Rock me, baby, honey, rock me slow.
   Hey, rock me, pretty baby, baby, rock me slow.
   Will you rock me, baby, 'til I want no more?

Satin Doll

Words by Johnny Mercer and Billy Strayhorn
Music by Duke Ellington

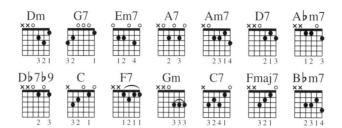

Strum Pattern: 4
Pick Pattern: 1

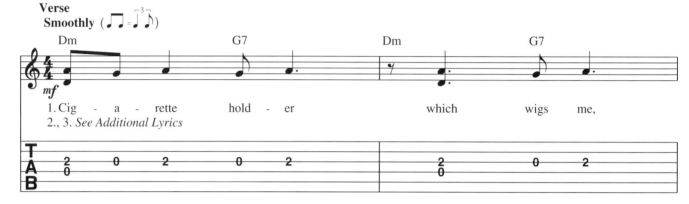

1. Cig - a - rette hold - er which wigs me,
2., 3. *See Additional Lyrics*

o - ver her shoul - der, she digs me.

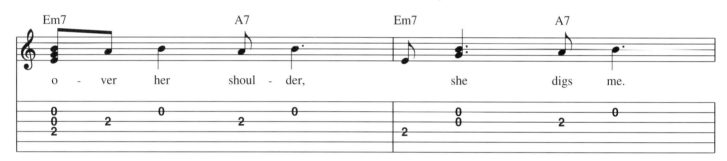

To Coda ⊕ | 1.

Out cat - tin' that sat - in doll. ____

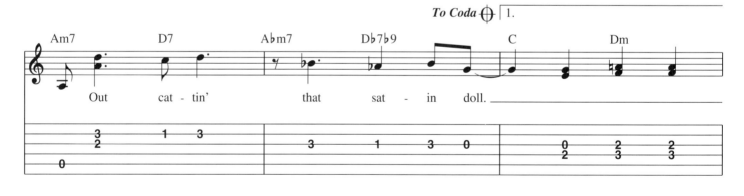

| 2.

She's

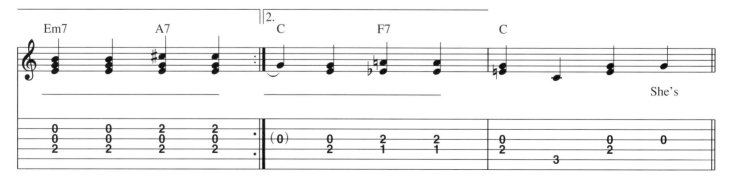

Bridge

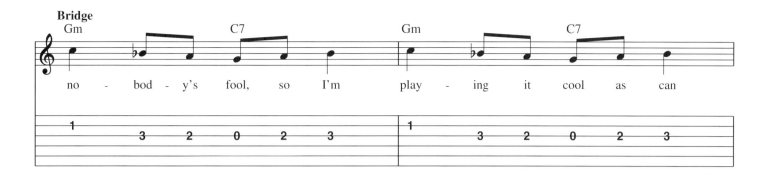

no - bod - y's fool, so I'm play - ing it cool as can

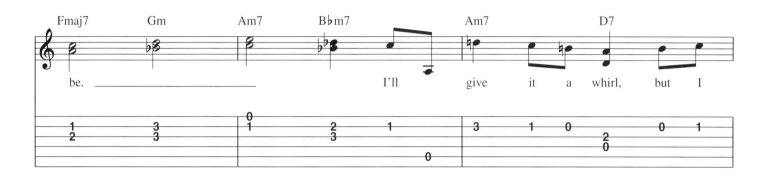

be. _____ I'll give it a whirl, but I

D.C. al Coda

ain't for no girl ____ catch - ing me. _____

⊕ *Coda*

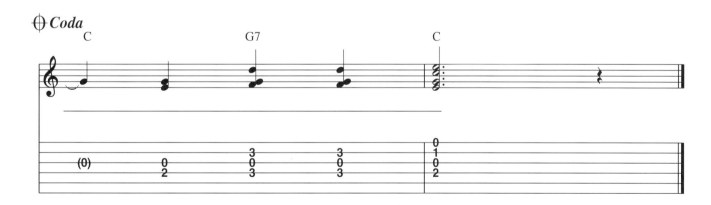

Additional Lyrics

2. Baby shall we go out skippin'?
   Careful amigo, you're flippin'.
   Speaks Latin, that satin doll.

3. Telephone numbers well you know,
   Doin' my rhumbas with uno,
   And that 'n' my satin doll.

Signs

Words and Music by Les Emmerson

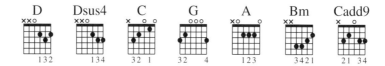

Strum Pattern: 4, 5
Pick Pattern: 1, 5

Intro
Moderately slow

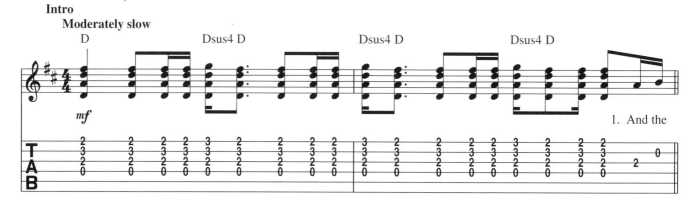

1. And the

Verse

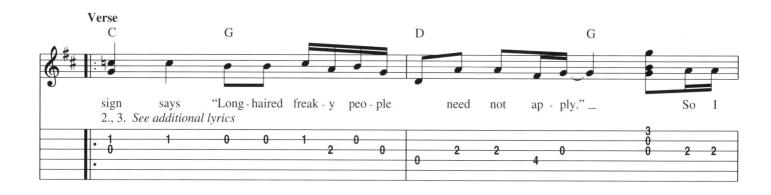

sign   says   "Long-haired freak-y peo-ple   need   not   ap-ply." __   So I
2., 3. *See additional lyrics*

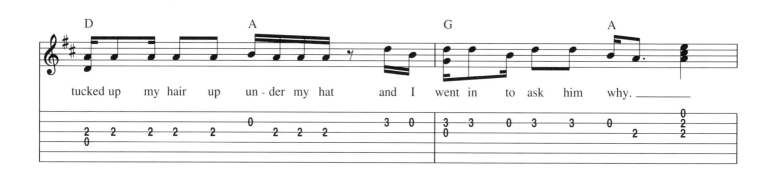

tucked up   my hair   up un-der my hat   and I went in to ask him why. _____

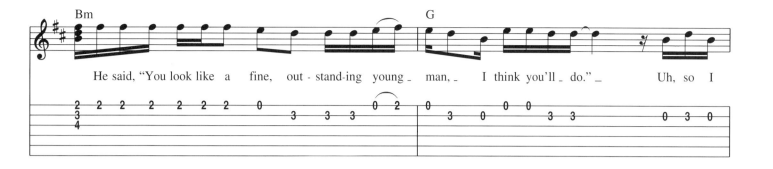

He said, "You look like a fine, out-stand-ing young _ man, _ I think you'll _ do." _ Uh, so I

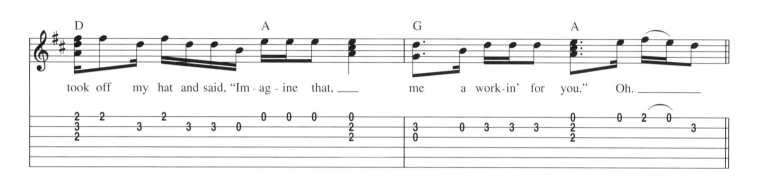

took off my hat and said, "Im-ag-ine that, ___ me a work-in' for you." Oh. _____

Chorus

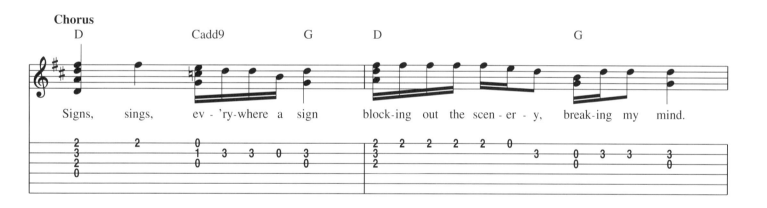

Signs, sings, ev-'ry-where a sign block-ing out the scen-er-y, break-ing my mind.

To Coda ⊕ | 1.

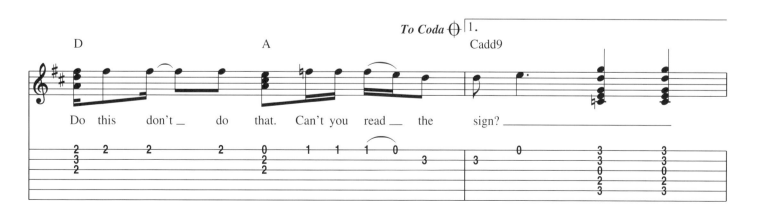

Do this don't _ do that. Can't you read _ the sign? _____

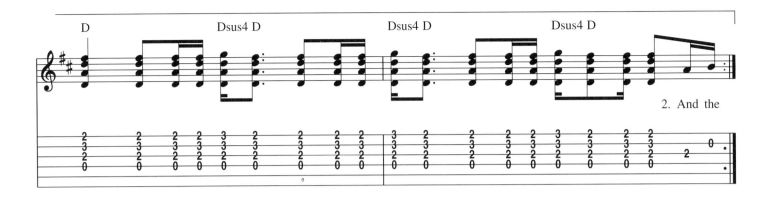

2. And the

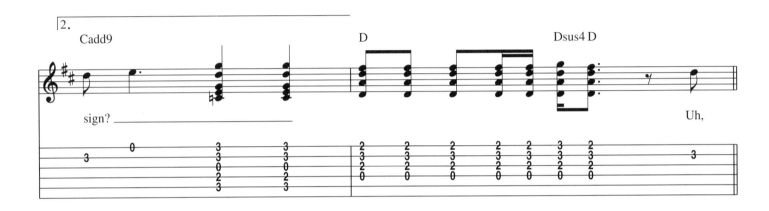

sign? _____ Uh,

Bridge

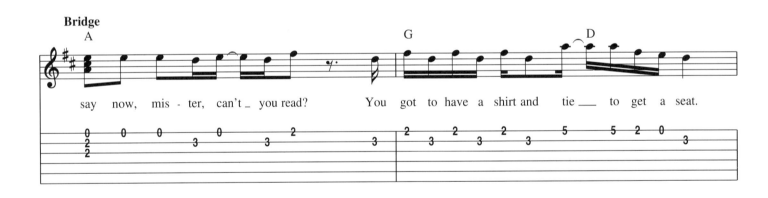

say now, mis - ter, can't _ you read? You got to have a shirt and tie ___ to get a seat.

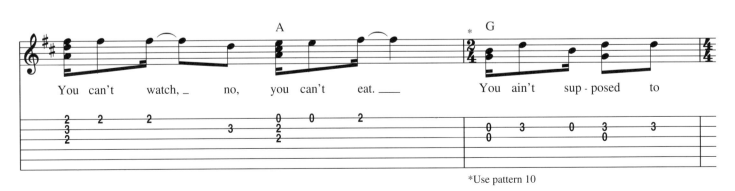

You can't watch, _ no, you can't eat. ___ You ain't sup - posed to

*Use pattern 10

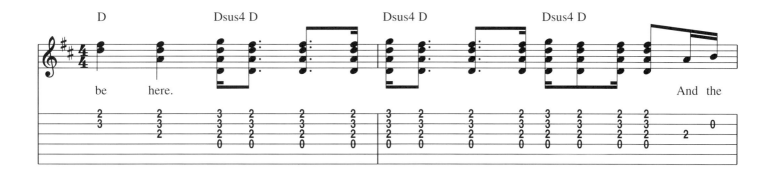

D.C. al Coda

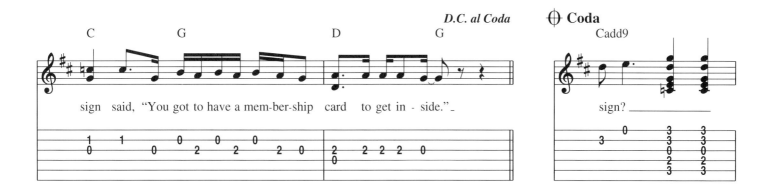

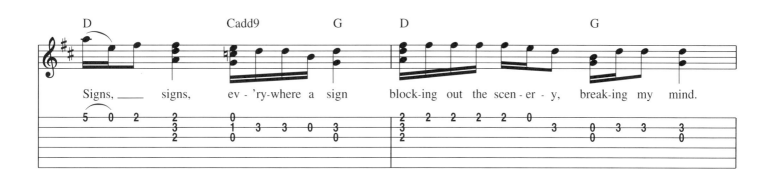

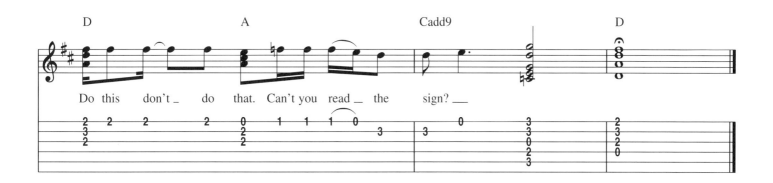

Additional Lyrics

2. And the sign says, "Anybody caught trespassing will be shot on sight."
   So I jumped the fence and yelled at the house, "Hey, what gives you the right
   To put up a fence to keep me out or to keep Mother Nature in?"
   If God was here he'd tell it to your face, "Man, you're some kinda sinner."

3. And the sign says, "Everybody welcome, come in and kneel down and pray."
   And then they pass around the plate at the end of it all, and I didn't have a penny to pay.
   So I got me a pen and paper, and I made up my own little sign.
   I said, "Thank you, Lord, for thinkin' about me, I'm alive and doing fine."

Southern Cross

Words and Music by Stephen Stills, Richard Curtis and Michael Curtis

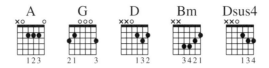

Strum Pattern: 5
Pick Pattern: 6

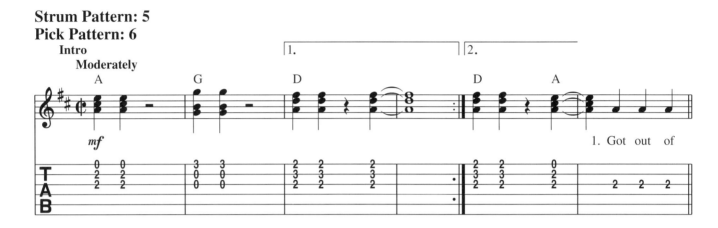

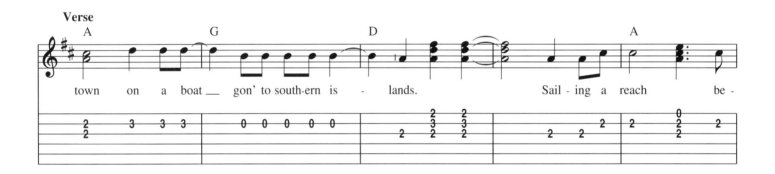

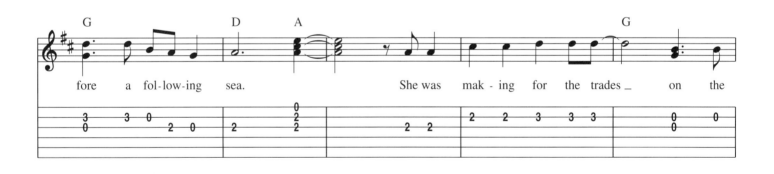

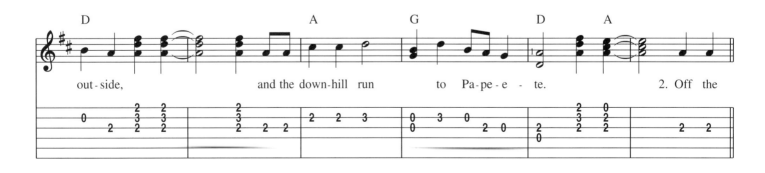

Verse

wind on this hea-ding, lie ___ the Mar - que - sas. We got eight - y feet _ of
4. *See Additional Lyrics*

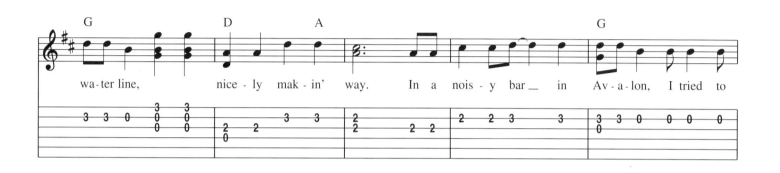

wa - ter line, nice - ly mak - in' way. In a nois - y bar _ in Av - a - lon, I tried to

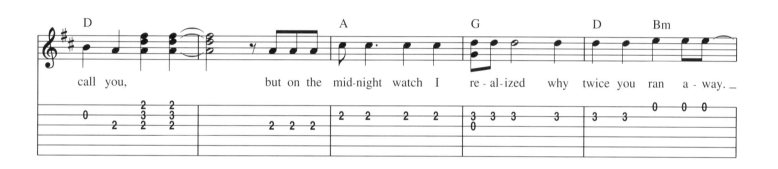

call you, but on the mid-night watch I re - al - ized why twice you ran a - way. _

Pre-Chorus

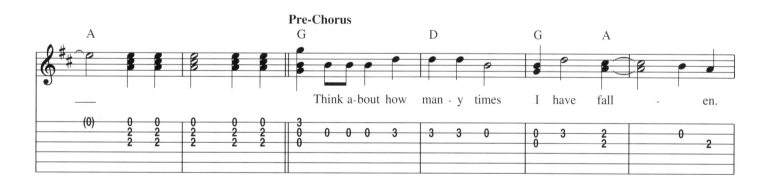

___ Think a - bout how man - y times I have fall - en.

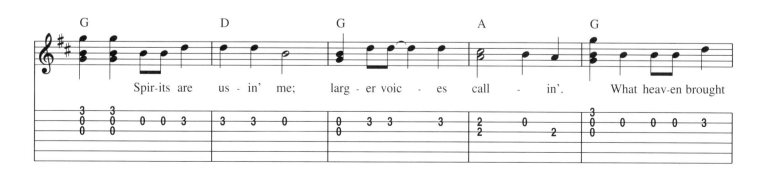

Spir - its are us - in' me; larg - er voic - es call - in'. What heav - en brought

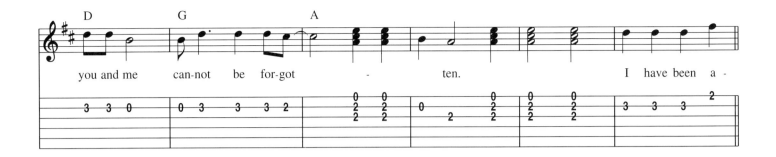

you and me can-not be for-got - ten. I have been a -

Chorus

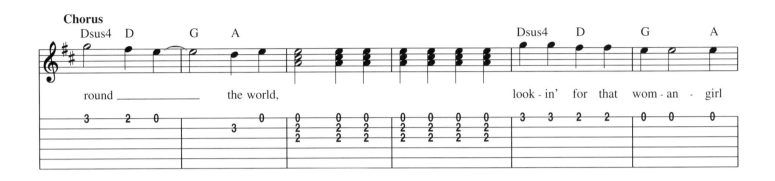

round _____ the world, look - in' for that wom - an - girl

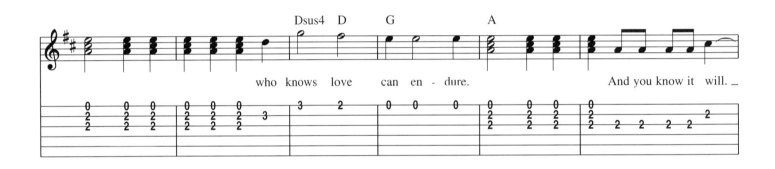

who knows love can en - dure. And you know it will. _

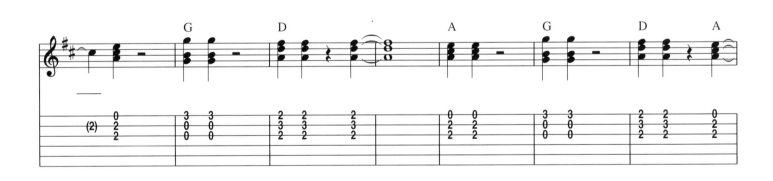

Verse

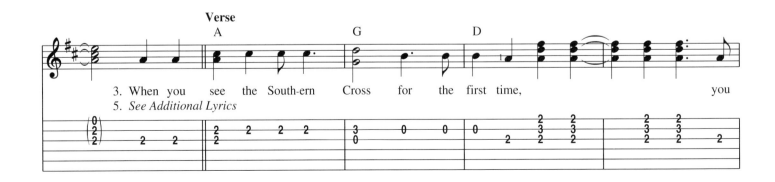

3. When you see the South-ern Cross for the first time, you
5. *See Additional Lyrics*

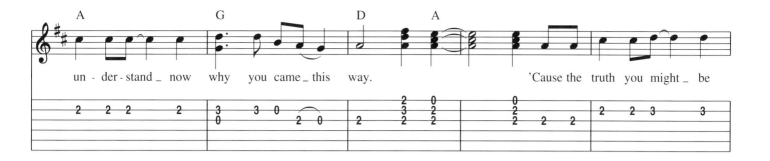

un - der - stand _ now why you came _ this way. 'Cause the truth you might _ be

run-nin' from is so small, but it's as big as the prom-ise, _ the

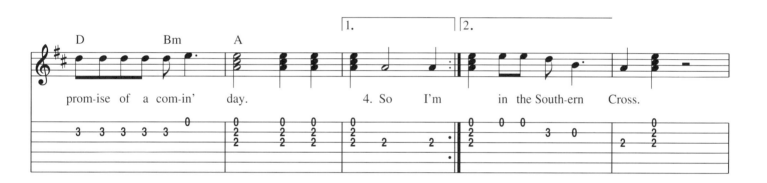

prom-ise of a com-in' day. 4. So I'm in the South-ern Cross.

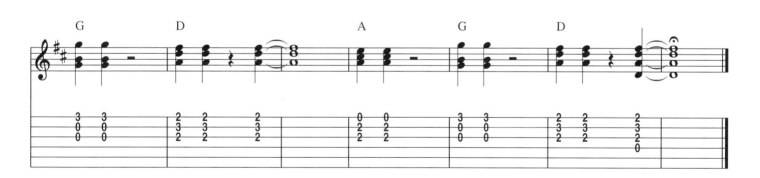

Additional Lyrics

4. So I'm sailing for tomorrow. My dreams are a-dying.
   And my love is an anchor tied to you, tied with a silver chain.
   I have my ship, and all her flags are a-flying.
   She is all that I have left, and music is her name.

5. So we cheated and we lied and we tested.
   And we never failed to fail; it was the easiest thing to do.
   You will survive being bested.
   Somebody fine will come along, make me forget about loving you
   In the Southern Cross.

Stand by Me

Words and Music by Ben E. King, Jerry Leiber and Mike Stoller

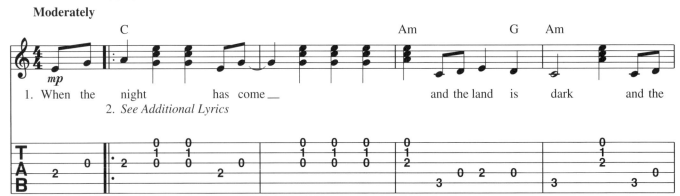

Strum Pattern: 2
Pick Pattern: 4

Verse
Moderately

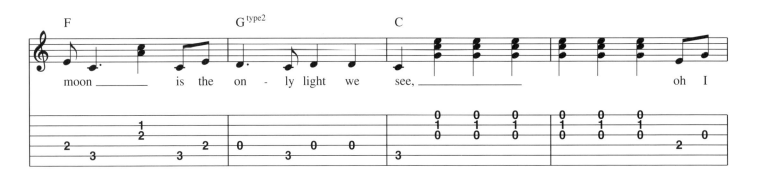

1. When the night has come ___ and the land is dark and the
2. *See Additional Lyrics*

moon _____ is the on - ly light we see, _____ oh I

won't be a-fraid, ___ no I _____ won't be a - fraid _____ just as

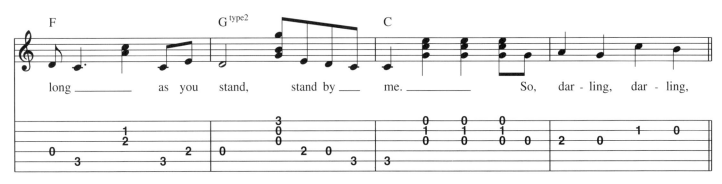

long _____ as you stand, stand by ___ me. _____ So, dar - ling, dar - ling,

Chorus

Additional Lyrics

2. If the sky that we look upon should tumble and fall
   And the mountains should crumble into the sea,
   I won't cry, I won't cry, no I won't shed a tear
   Just as long as you stand, stand by me.

Statesboro Blues

Words and Music by Willy McTell

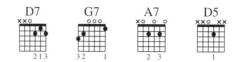

Strum Pattern: 1, 6
Pick Pattern: 2, 6

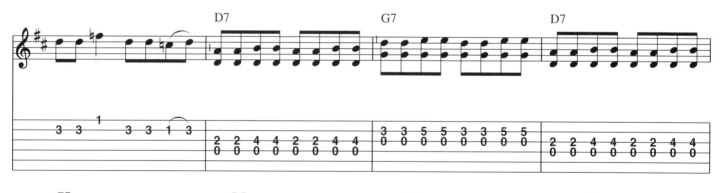

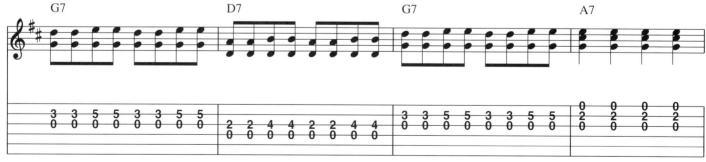

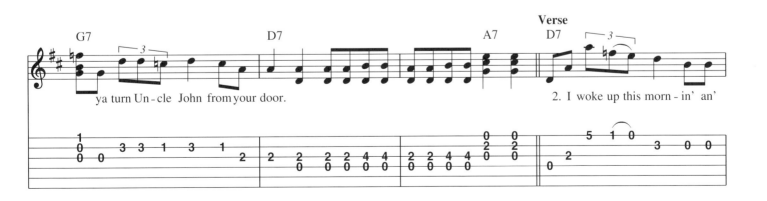

I had them States-bo-ro   blues. _   I woke up this morn-in' an'

I had them States-bo-ro   blues. _   Well, I looked o-ver in the   cor - ner, ba-by,

Interlude

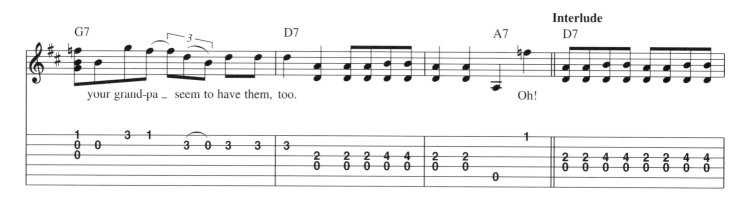

your grand-pa _ seem to have them, too.   Oh!

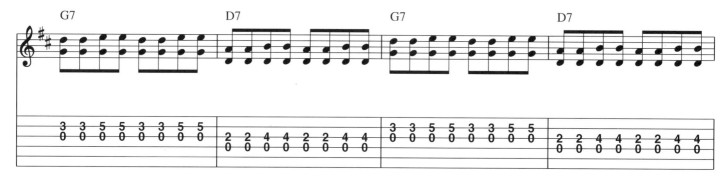

Verse

3. Well,   my ma-ma died and left me, my   pa-pa died and left me.   I ain't good look-in', ba-by,   want

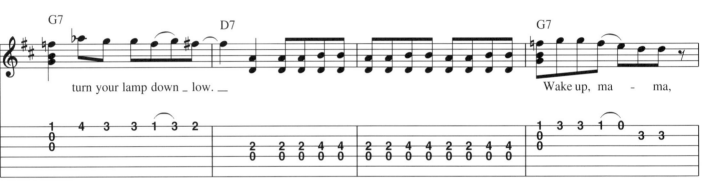

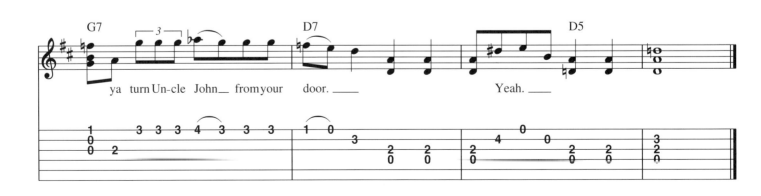

Sunshine of Your Love

Words and Music by Jack Bruce, Pete Brown and Eric Clapton

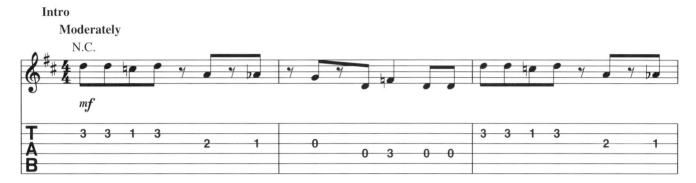

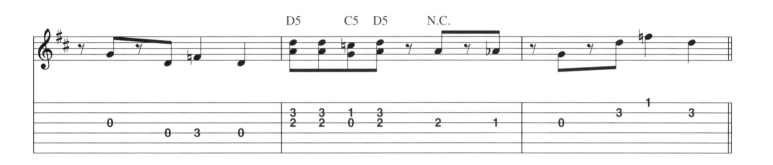

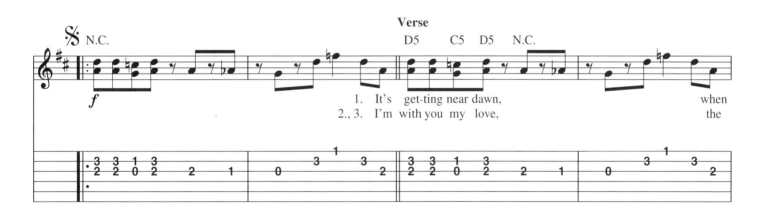

love, ___   to give you my dawn ___ sur - prise. ___   I'll
it's the morn - ing and just ___ we ___ two. ___   I'll

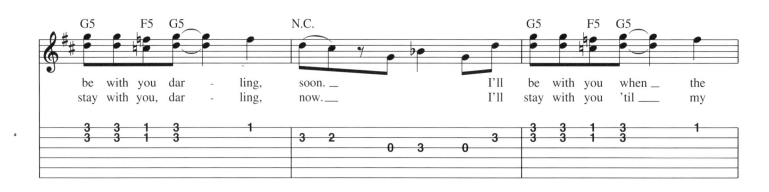

be with you dar - ling,   soon. ___   I'll be with you when ___ the
stay with you, dar - ling,   now. ___   I'll stay with you 'til ___ my

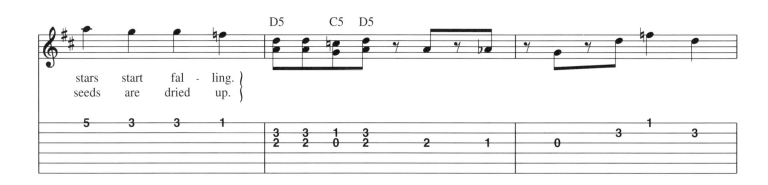

stars start fal - ling.
seeds are dried up.

To Coda ⊕

Chorus

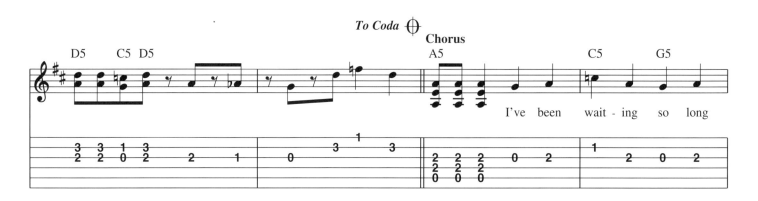

I've been wait - ing so long

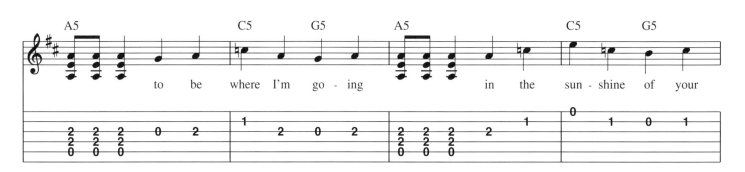

to be where I'm go - ing   in the sun - shine of your

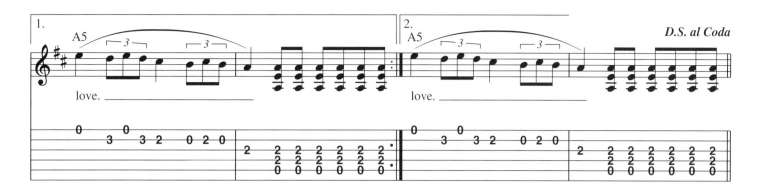

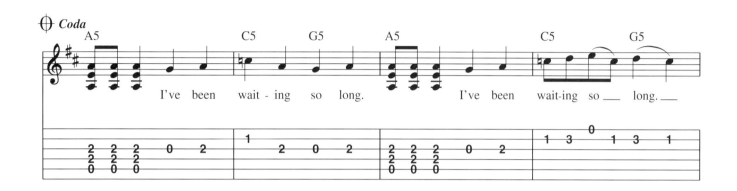

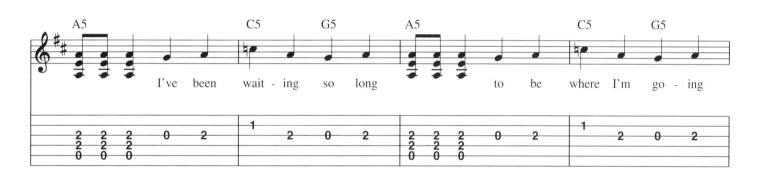

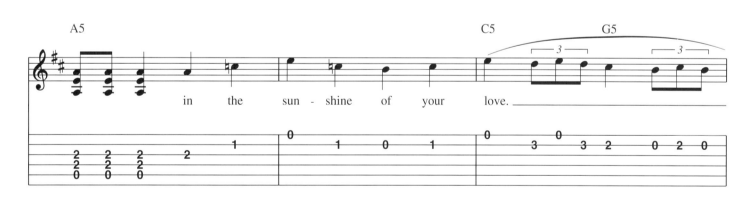

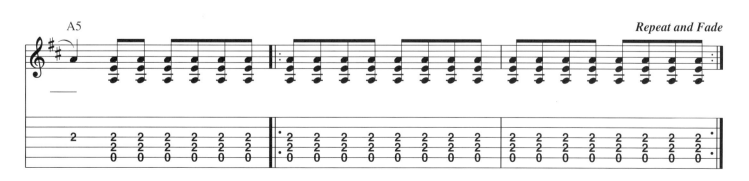

Surfin' U.S.A.

Words and Music by Chuck Berry

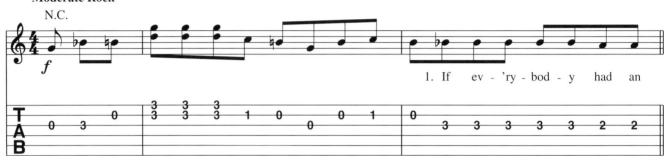

Strum Pattern: 1
Pick Pattern: 2

Intro
Moderate Rock

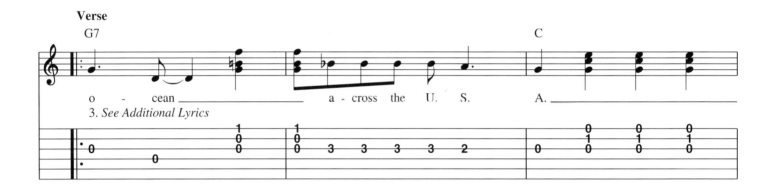

1. If ev - 'ry - bod - y had an

Verse

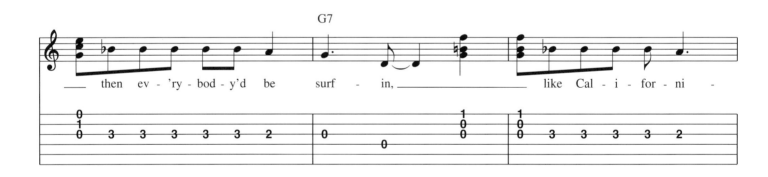

o - cean _____ a - cross the U. S. A. _____
3. *See Additional Lyrics*

_____ then ev - 'ry - bod - y'd be surf - in, _____ like Cal - i - for - ni -

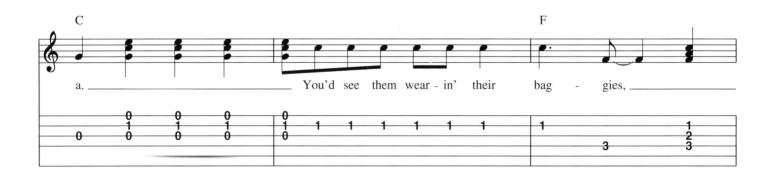

a. _____ You'd see them wear - in' their bag - gies, _____

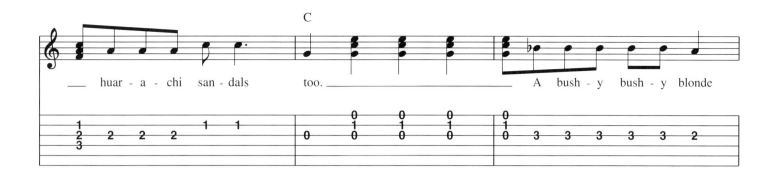

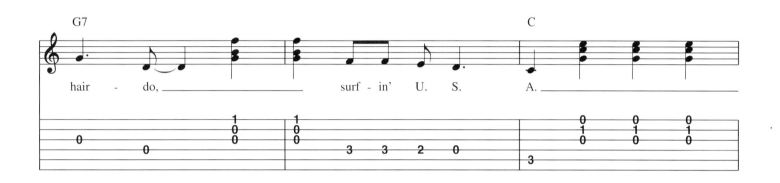

Verse

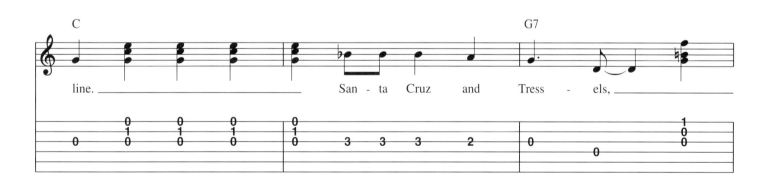

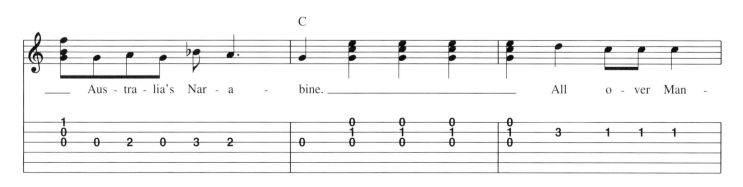

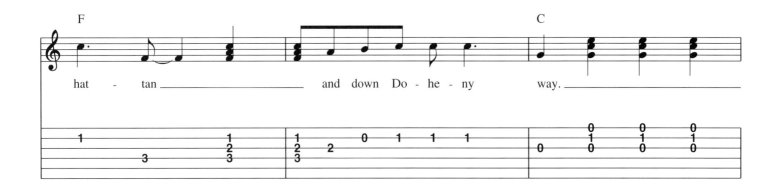

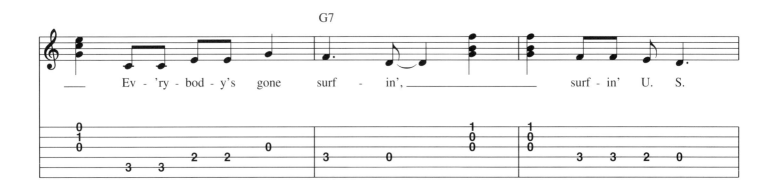

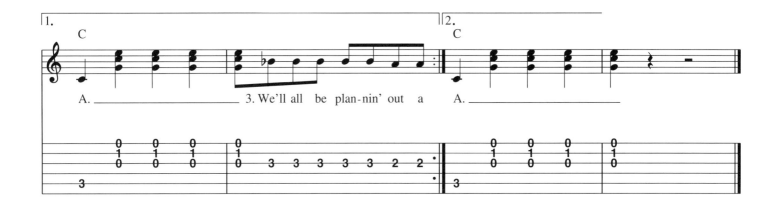

Additional Lyrics

3. We'll all be plannin' out a route
   Were gonna take real soon.
   We're waxin' down our surfboards,
   We can't wait for June.
   We'll all be gone for the summer,
   We're on safari to stay.
   Tell the teacher we're surfin',
   Surfin' U.S.A.

4. At Haggarty's and Swami's
   Pacific Palisades.
   San Onfre and Sunset,
   Redondo Beach L.A.
   All over La Jolla,
   at Waiamea Bay.
   Ev'rybody's gone surfin',
   Surfin' U.S.A.

Tears in Heaven

Words and Music by Eric Clapton and Will Jennings

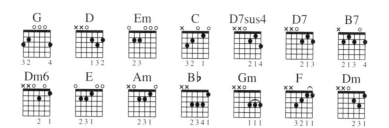

Strum Pattern: 6
Pick Pattern: 4

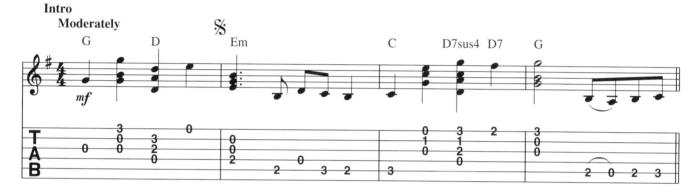

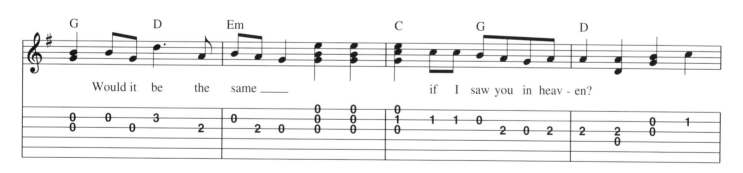

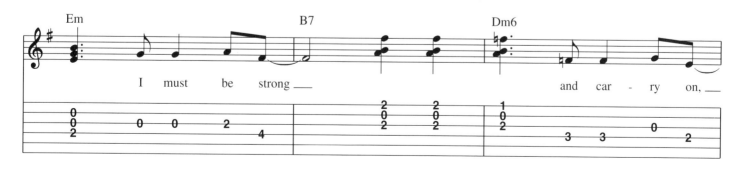

'cause I know I don't be - long _____ here in heav -

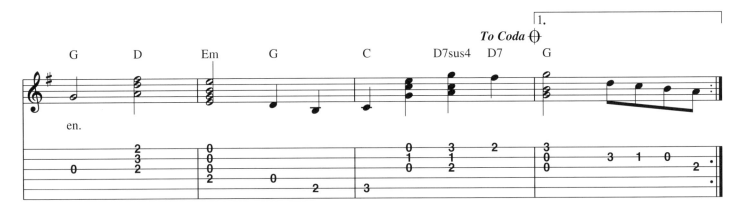

To Coda ⊕

1.

en.

2.

Bridge

Time can bring you down, __ time can bend your

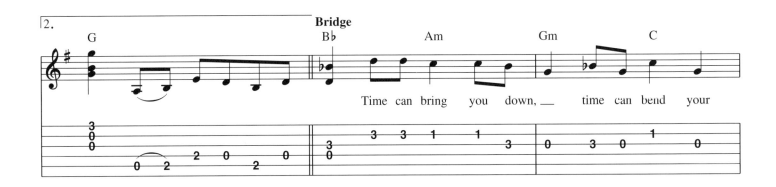

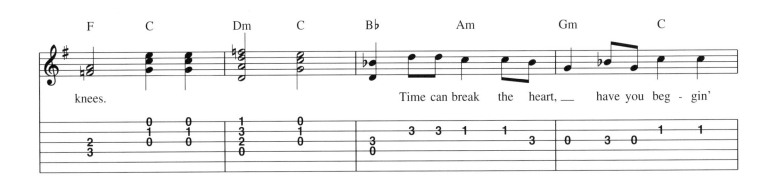

knees. Time can break the heart, __ have you beg - gin'

Guitar Solo

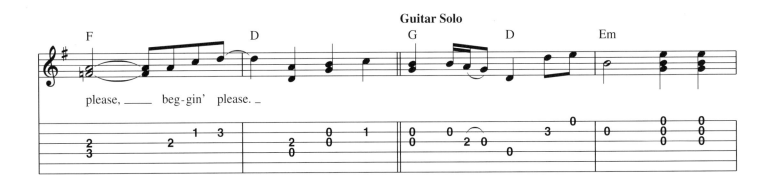

please, __ beg-gin' please. __

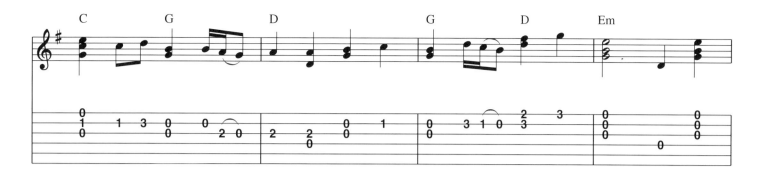

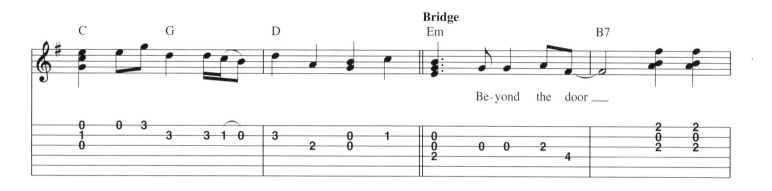

Be-yond the door ___

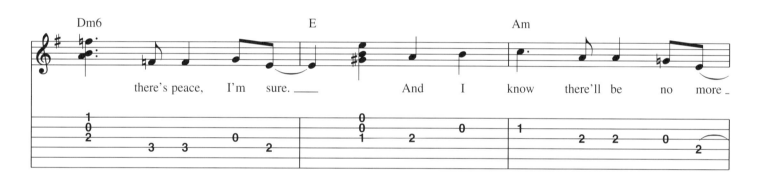

there's peace, I'm sure. ___ And I know there'll be no more ___

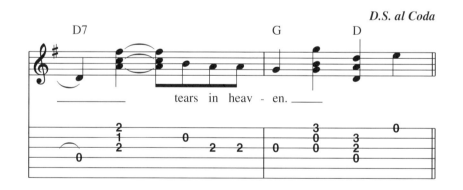

tears in heav - en. ___

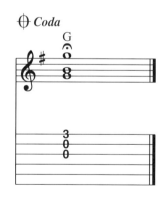

Additional Lyrics

2. Would you hold my hand
   If I saw you in heaven?
   Would you help me stand
   If I saw you in heaven?
   I'll find my way through night and day,
   'Cause I know I just can't stay here in heaven.

Take the "A" Train

Words and Music by Billy Strayhorn

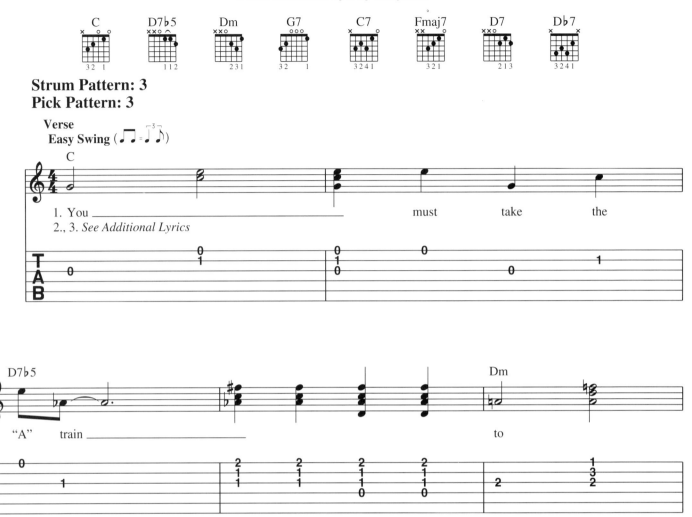

Strum Pattern: 3
Pick Pattern: 3

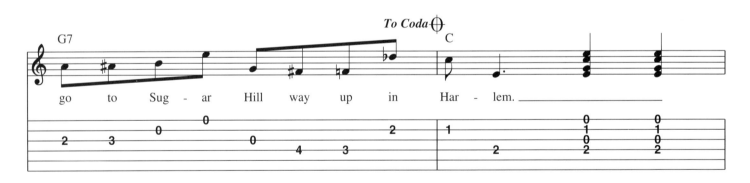

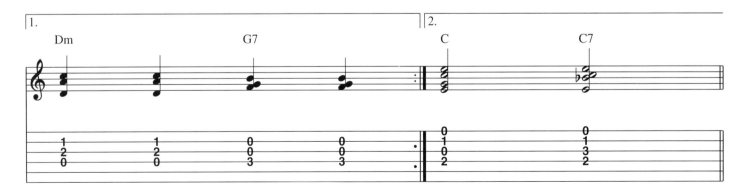

Bridge

Hur - ry, _____ get on now it's com - ing. _____

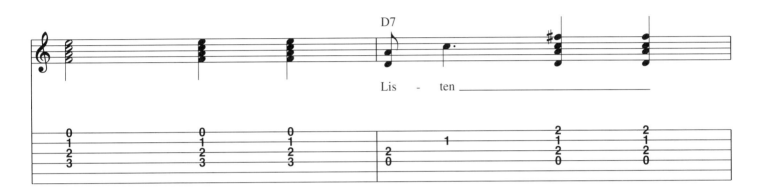

Lis - ten _____

D.C. al Coda

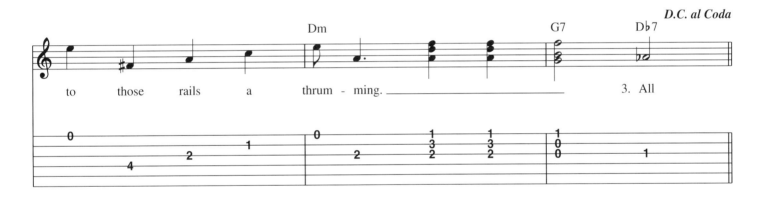

to those rails a thrum - ming. _____ 3. All

⊕ *Coda*

Har - lem.

Additional Lyrics

2. If you miss the "A" train,
   You'll find you've missed the quickest way to Harlem.

3. All 'board! Get on the "A" train.
   Soon you'll be on Sugar Hill in Harlem.

Takin' Care of Business

Words and Music by Randy Bachman

tak - ing care of busi - ness, it's all mine. Tak - ing care of busi - ness and

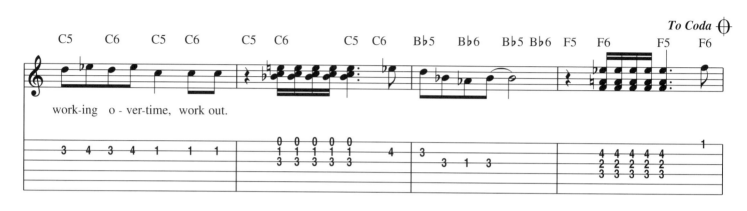

To Coda

work-ing o - ver-time, work out.

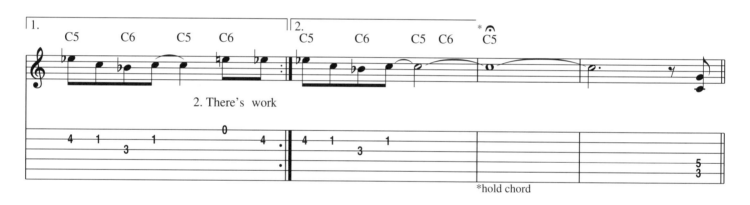

1.

2.

2. There's work

*hold chord

Bridge

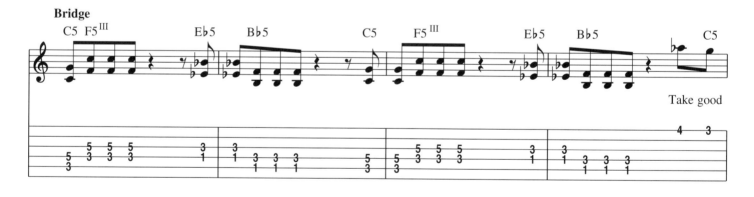

Take good

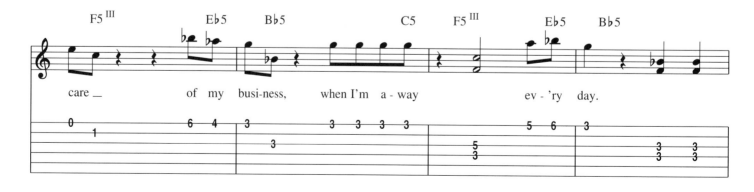

care ___ of my busi-ness, when I'm a - way ev - 'ry day.

Additional Lyrics

2. There's work easy as fishin',
   You could be a musician
   If you could make sounds loud or mellow.
   Get a second hand guitar,
   Chances are you'll go far
   If you get in with the right bunch of fellows.
   People see you having fun,
   Just a-lying in the sun.
   Tell them that you like it this way.
   It's the work that we avoid
   And we're all self-employed.
   We love to work at nothing all day.

Tennessee Waltz

Words and Music by Redd Stewart and Pee Wee King

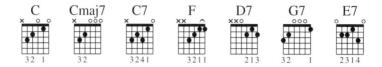

Strum Pattern: 8
Pick Pattern: 8

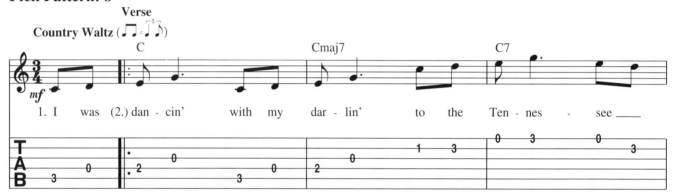

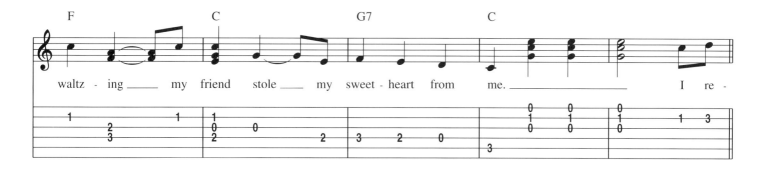

waltz - ing ____ my friend stole ____ my sweet - heart from me. _____ I re -

Chorus

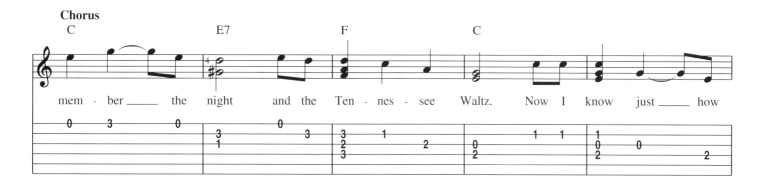

mem - ber ____ the night and the Ten - nes - see Waltz. Now I know just ____ how

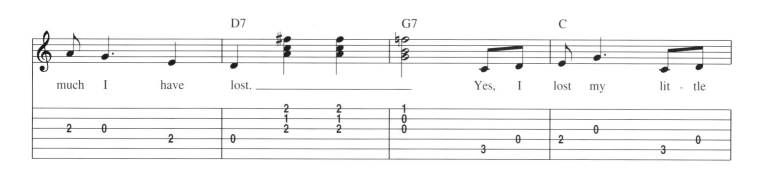

much I have lost. _____ Yes, I lost my lit - tle

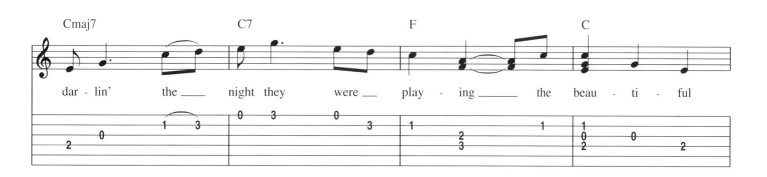

dar - lin' the ____ night they were ____ play - ing ____ the beau - ti - ful

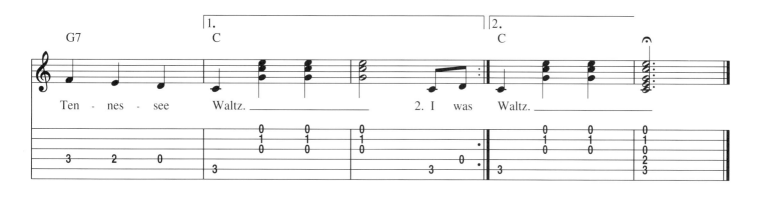

Ten - nes - see Waltz. _____ 2. I was Waltz. _____

That'll Be the Day

Words and Music by Jerry Allison, Norman Petty and Buddy Holly

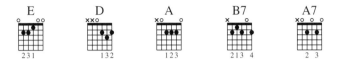

Strum Pattern: 1
Pick Pattern: 2

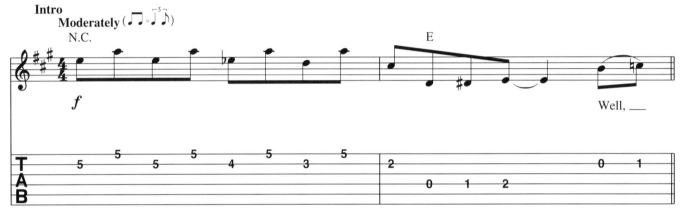

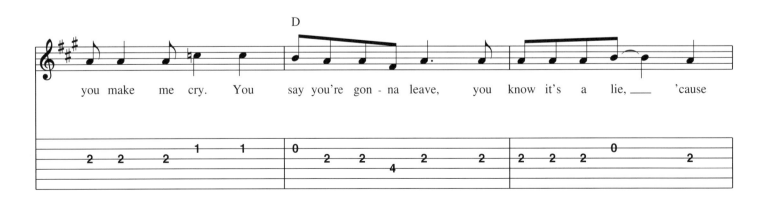

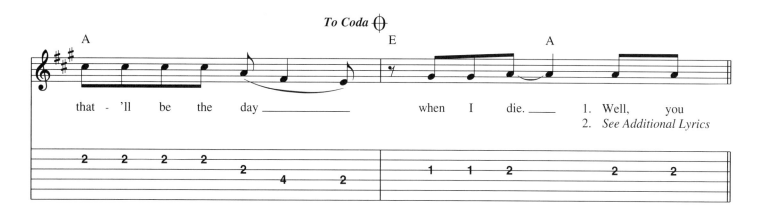

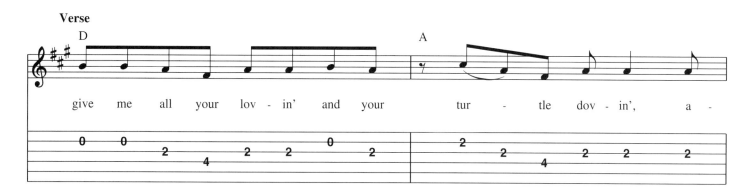

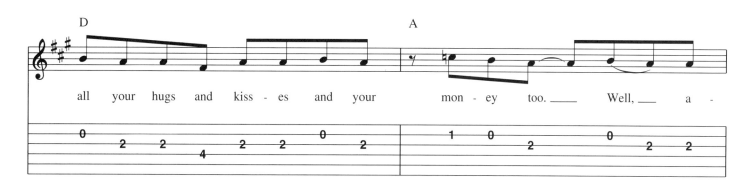

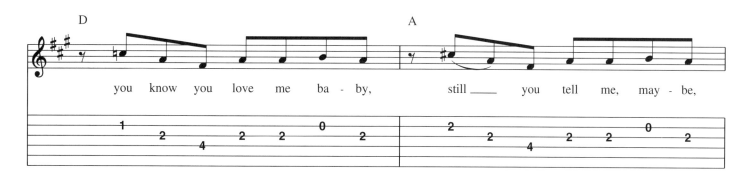

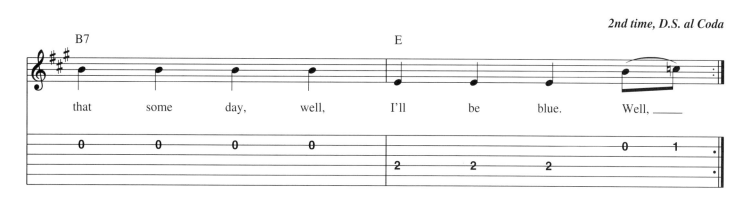

⊕ *Coda*

when I die. ___ Well, ___ that-'ll be the day, ooh. ___

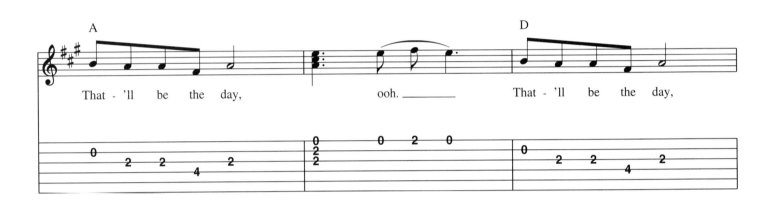

That-'ll be the day, ooh. ___ That-'ll be the day,

ooh. ___ That-'ll be the day.

Additional Lyrics

2. Well, when cupid shot his dart,
   He shot it at your heart,
   So if we ever part then I'll leave you.
   You sit and hold me and you
   Tell me boldly, that some day,
   Well, I'll be through.

Twist and Shout

Words and Music by Bert Russell and Phil Medley

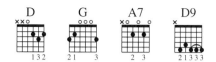

Strum Pattern: 6
Pick Pattern: 6

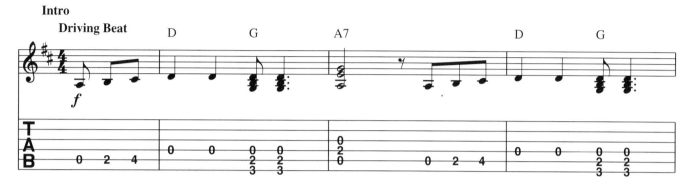

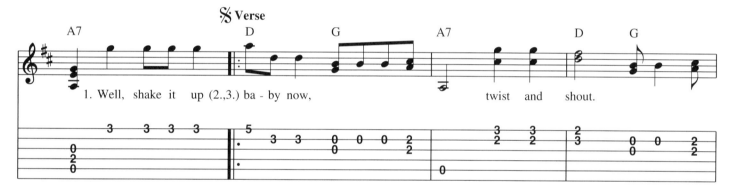

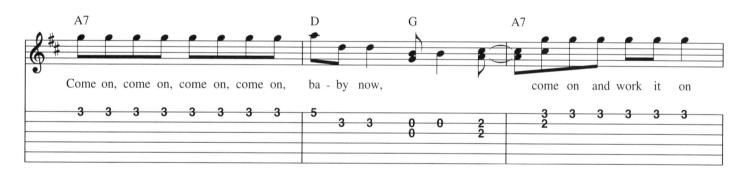

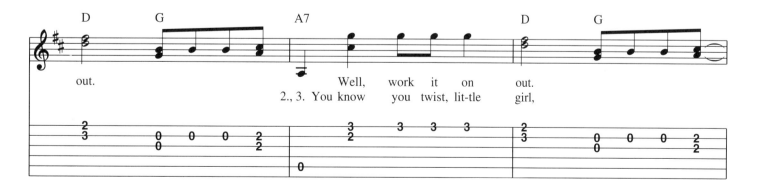

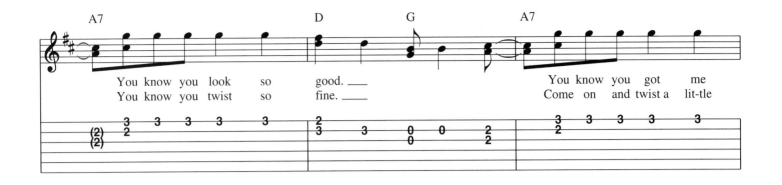

You know you look   so   good. ___
You know you twist   so   fine. ___
You know you got   me
Come on   and twist a   lit-tle

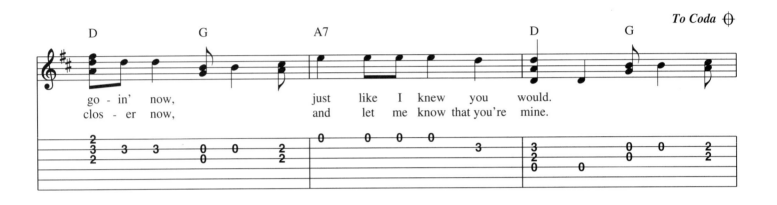

To Coda ⊕

go - in'   now,
clos - er   now,
just   like   I   knew   you   would.
and   let   me   know that you're   mine.

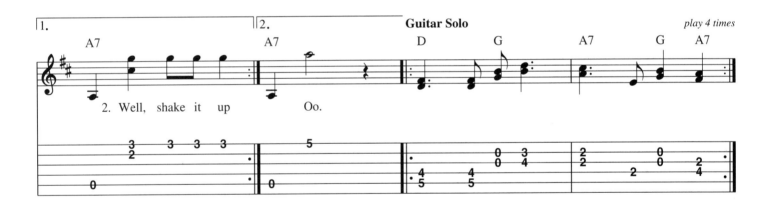

1.   2.   **Guitar Solo**   *play 4 times*

2. Well,   shake   it   up   Oo.

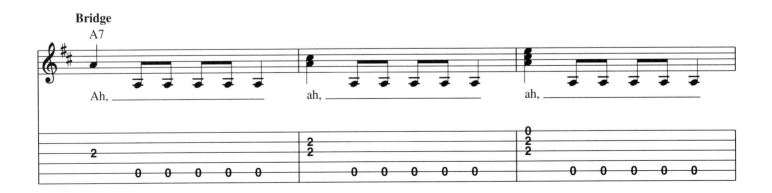

Bridge

Ah, _____   ah, _____   ah, _____

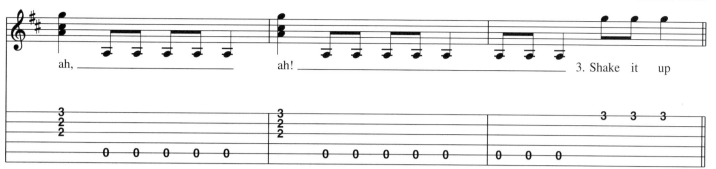

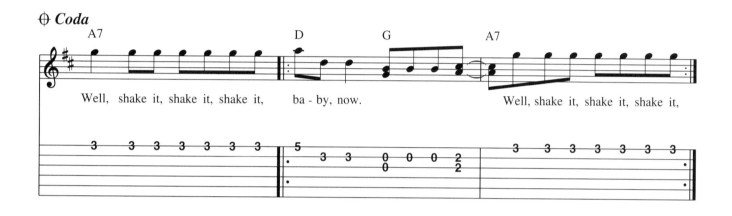

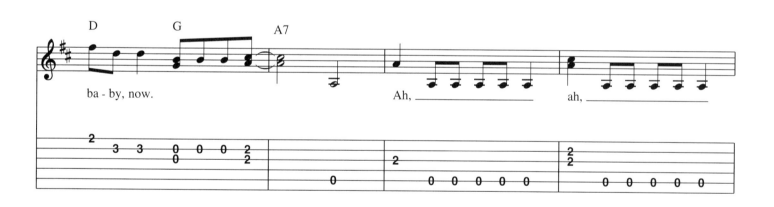

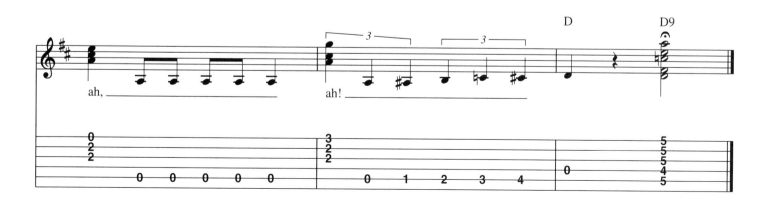

Time in a Bottle

Words and Music by Jim Croce

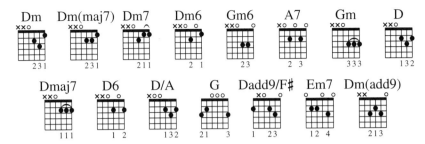

Strum Pattern: 9
Pick Pattern: 9

Intro
Moderately

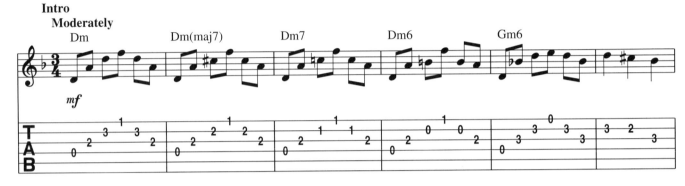

%% Verse

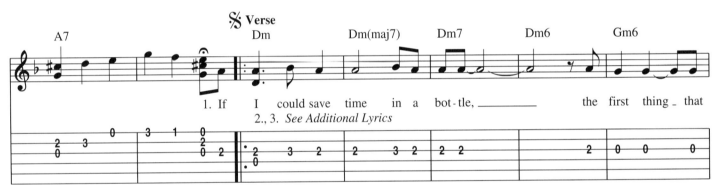

1. If I could save time in a bot-tle, _____ the first thing _ that
2., 3. *See Additional Lyrics*

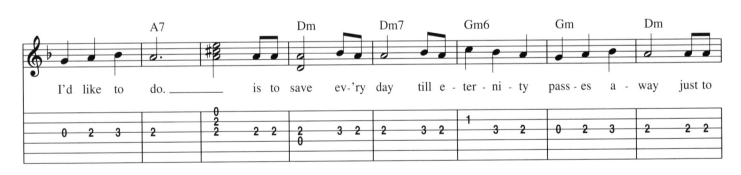

I'd like to do. _____ is to save ev-'ry day till e-ter-ni-ty pass-es a-way just to

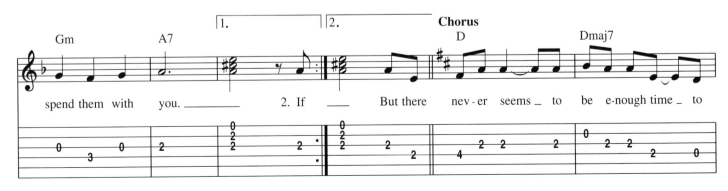

spend them with you. _____ 2. If ___ But there nev-er seems _ to be e-nough time _ to

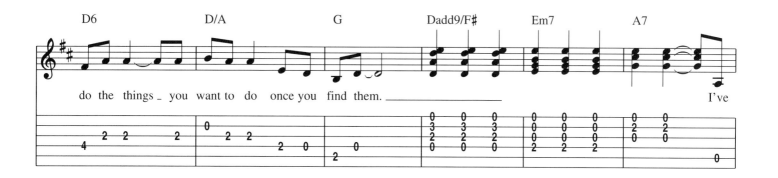

do the things _ you want to do once you find them. _____ I've

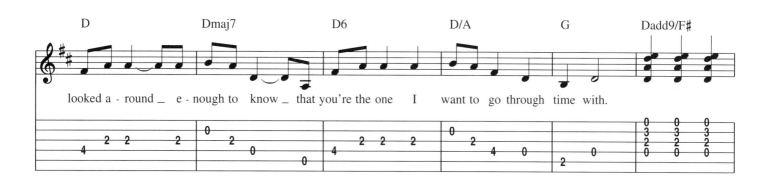

looked a - round _ e - nough to know _ that you're the one I want to go through time with.

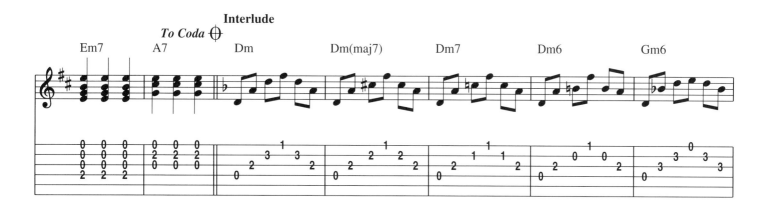

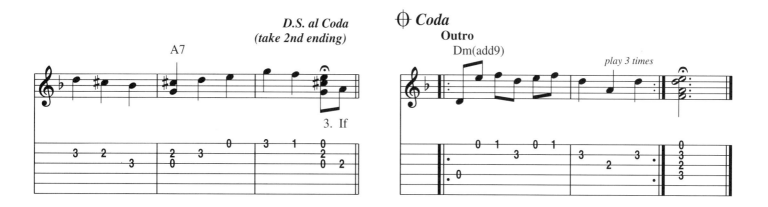

3. If

Additional Lyrics

2. If I could make days last forever,
   If words could make wishes come true,
   I'd save ev'ry day like a treasure, and then
   Again I would spend them with you.

3. If I had a box just for wishes,
   And dreams that had never come true,
   The box would be empty except for the mem'ry
   Of how they were answered by you.

Tulsa Time

Words and Music by Danny Flowers

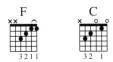

Strum Pattern: 4

Intro

Moderate Country ♩ = 120

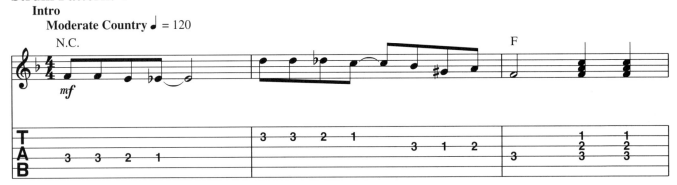

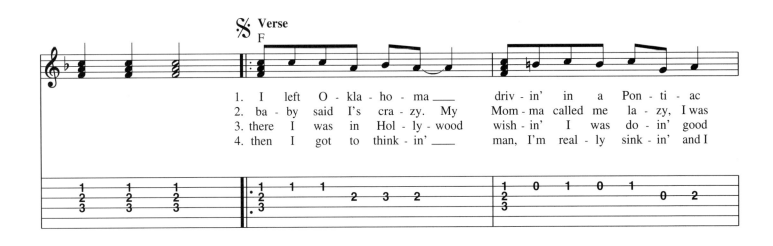

1. I left O - kla - ho - ma ___ driv - in' in a Pon - ti - ac
2. ba - by said I's cra - zy. My Mom - ma called me la - zy, I was
3. there I was in Hol - ly - wood wish - in' I was do - in' good
4. then I got to think - in' ___ man, I'm real - ly sink - in' and I

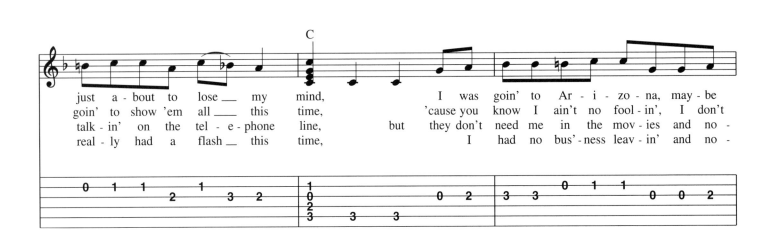

just a - bout to lose ___ my mind, I was goin' to Ar - i - zo - na, may - be
goin' to show 'em all ___ this time, 'cause you know I ain't no fool - in', I don't
talk - in' on the tel - e - phone line, but they don't need me in the mov - ies and no
real - ly had a flash ___ this time, I had no bus' - ness leav - in' and no -

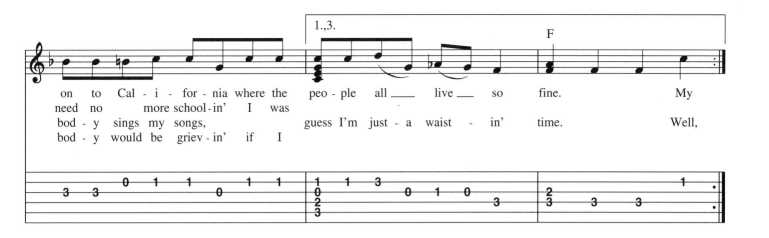

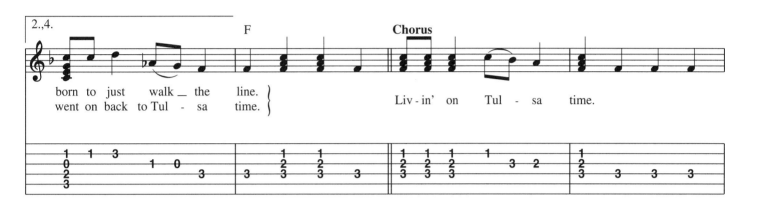

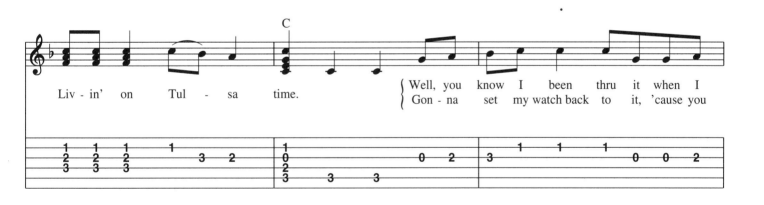

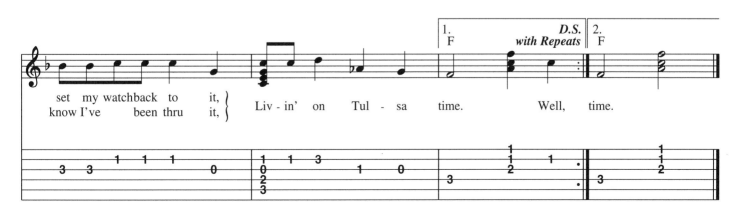

Unchained Melody

Lyric by Hy Zaret
Music by Alex North

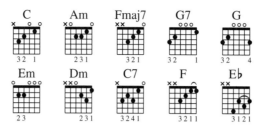

Strum Pattern: 4
Pick Pattern: 2

Verse
Slowly

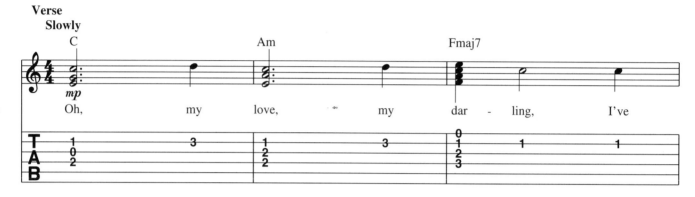

Oh, my love, my dar - ling, I've

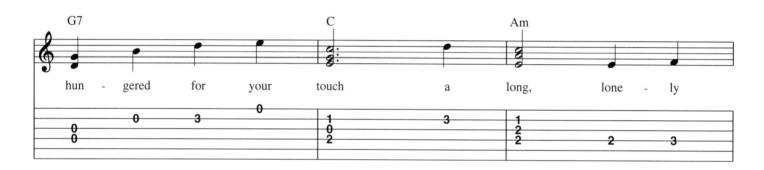

hun - gered for your touch a long, lone - ly

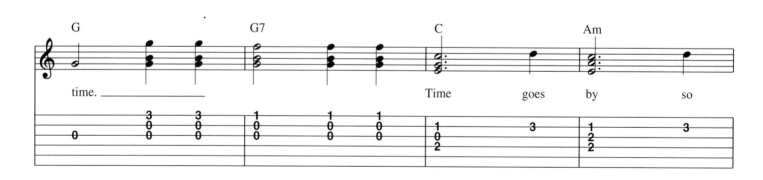

time. Time goes by so

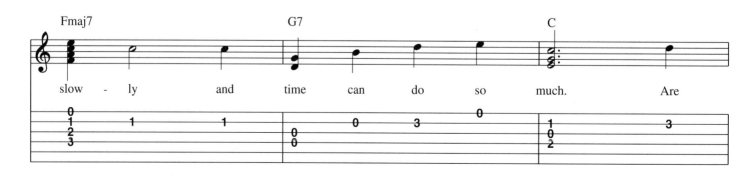

slow - ly and time can do so much. Are

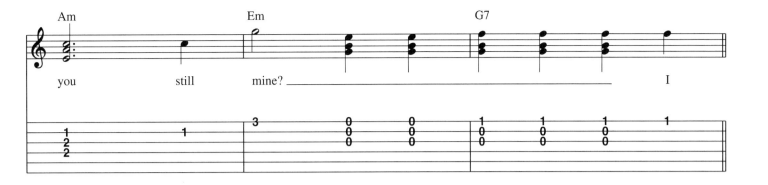

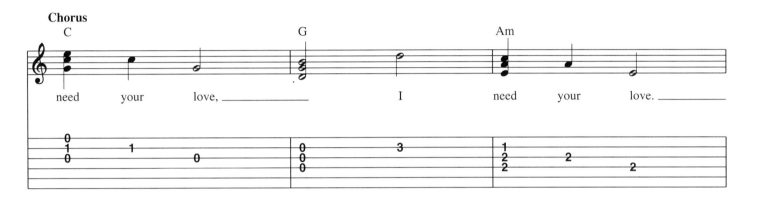

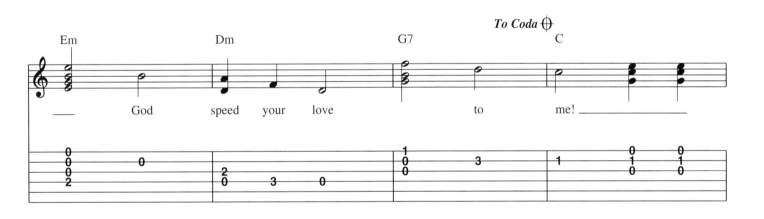

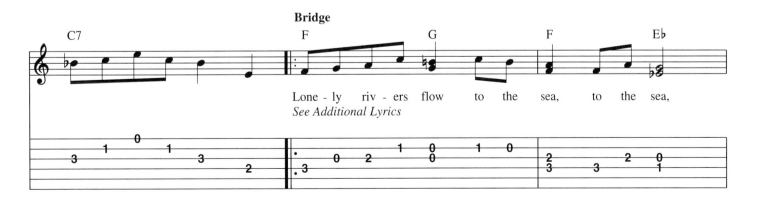

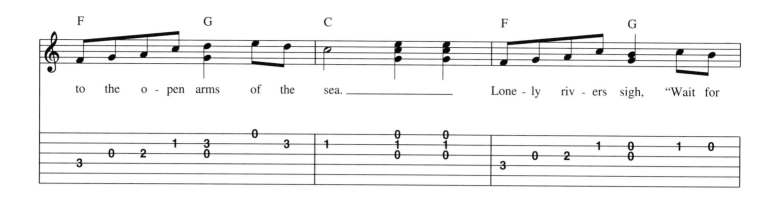

to the o - pen arms of the sea. _____ Lone - ly riv - ers sigh, "Wait for

me, wait for me!" I'll be com - ing home, wait for me. _____

2nd time, D.C. al Coda

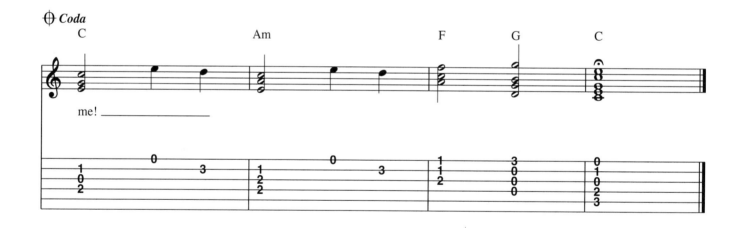

me! _____

Additional Lyrics

Bridge   Lonely mountains gaze
At the stars, at the stars,
Waiting for the dawn of the day.
All alone, I gaze
At the stars, at the stars,
Dreaming of my love far away.

Wake Up Little Susie

Words and Music by Boudleaux Bryant and Felice Bryant

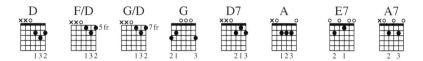

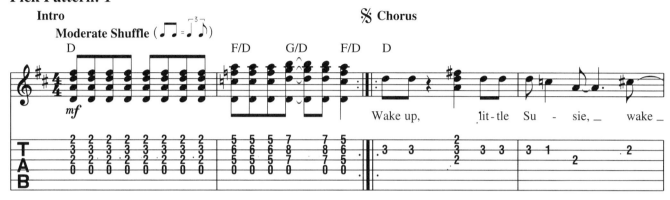

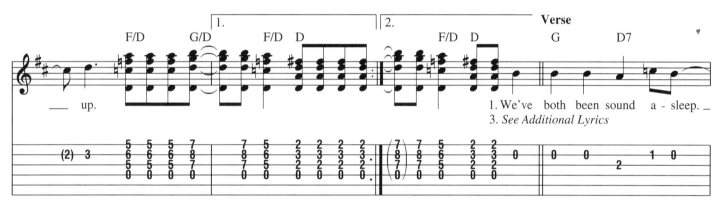

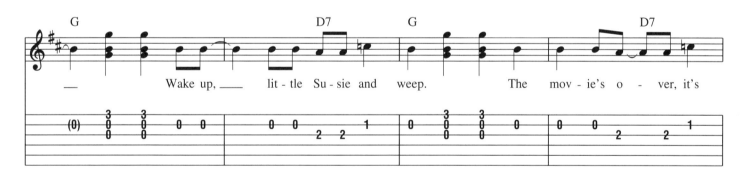

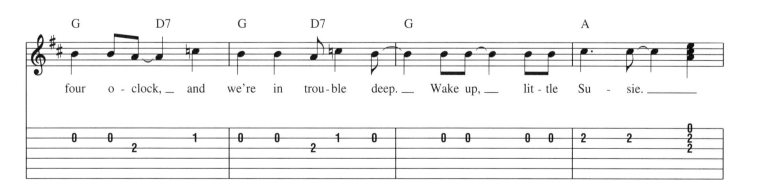

173

Wake up, ___ lit - tle Su - sie. _____ 2., 4. Well, what-'re we gon - na tell your ma -

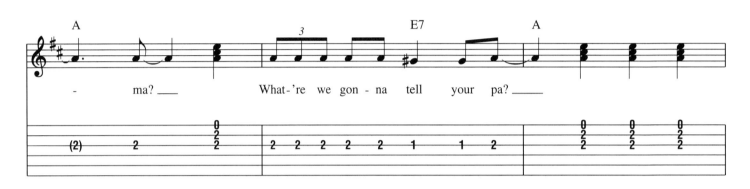

- ma? ___ What-'re we gon - na tell your pa? _____

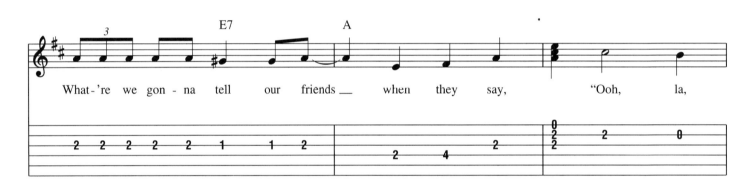

What-'re we gon - na tell our friends ___ when they say, "Ooh, la,

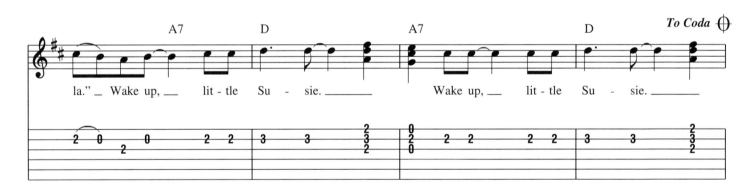

la." ___ Wake up, ___ lit - tle Su - sie. _____ Wake up, ___ lit - tle Su - sie. _____

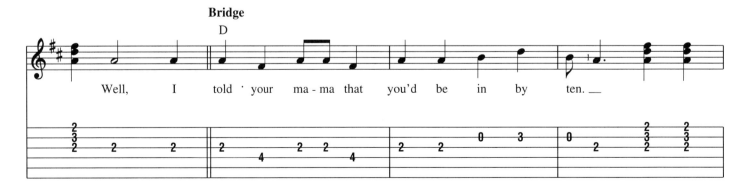

Well, I told your ma - ma that you'd be in by ten. ___

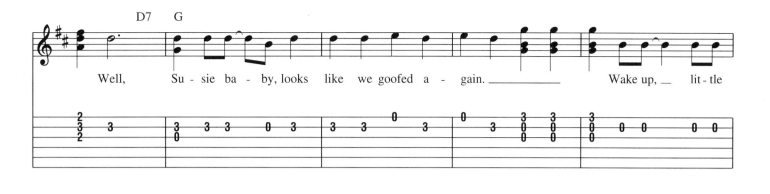

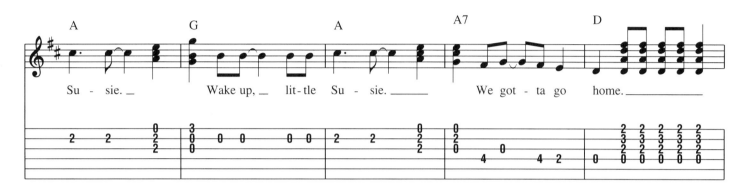

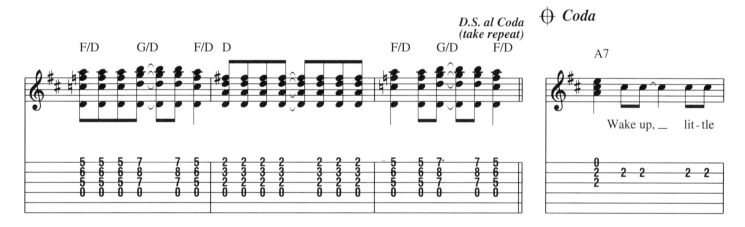

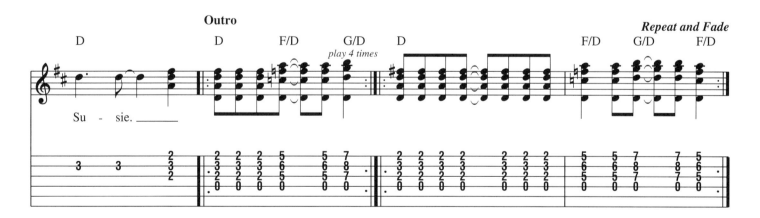

Additional Lyrics

3. The movie wasn't so hot.
   It didn't have much of a plot.
   We fell asleep, our goose is cooked,
   Our reputation is shot.
   Wake up, little Susie.
   Wake up, little Susie.

Walk This Way

Words and Music by Steven Tyler and Joe Perry

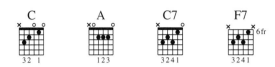

Strum Pattern: 3, 5
Pick Pattern: 3, 5

Intro
Lively

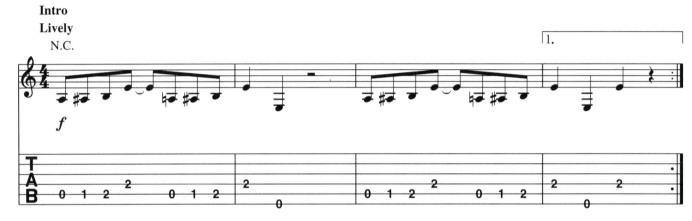

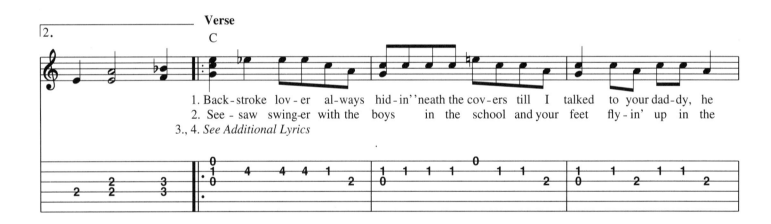

1. Back-stroke lov-er al-ways hid-in' 'neath the cov-ers till I talked to your dad-dy, he
2. See-saw swing-er with the boys in the school and your feet fly-in' up in the
3., 4. *See Additional Lyrics*

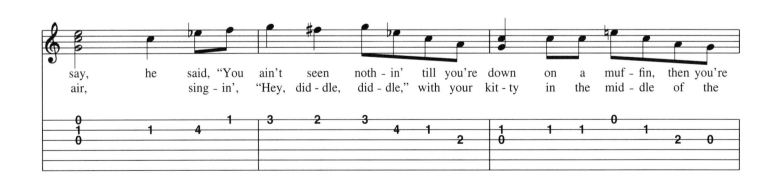

say, he said, "You ain't seen noth-in' till you're down on a muf-fin, then you're
air, sing-in', "Hey, did-dle, did-dle," with your kit-ty in the mid-dle of the

sure to be a-chang-in' your ways." I met a cheer - lead - er, was a
swing like you did-n't care. So I took a big chance at the

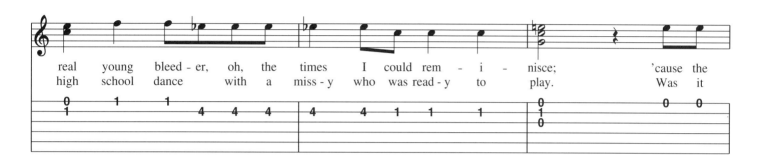

real young bleed - er, oh, the times I could rem - i - nisce; 'cause the
high school dance with a miss-y who was read-y to play. Was it

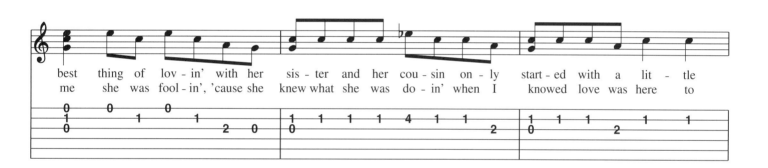

best thing of lov-in' with her sis - ter and her cou-sin on - ly start-ed with a lit-tle
me she was fool-in', 'cause she knew what she was do-in' when I knowed love was here to

1., 3.

kiss *like this.*

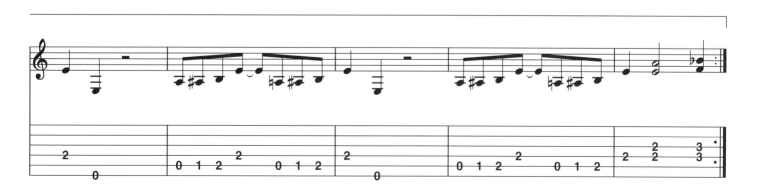

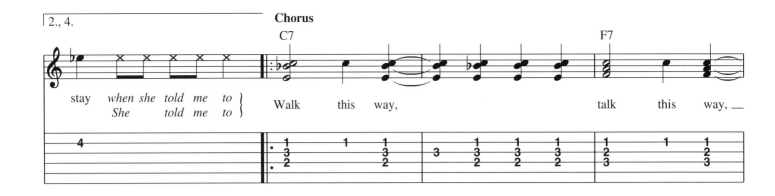

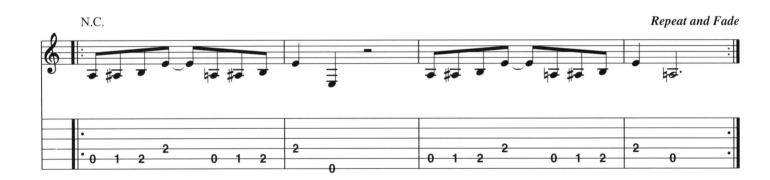

Additional Lyrics

3. School girl sweeties with a classy, kind-a sassy
   Little skirts climbin' way up their knee.
   There was three young ladies in the school gym locker
   When I noticed they was lookin' at me.
   I was a high school loser, never made it with a lady
   Till the boys told me somethin' I missed.
   Then my next door neighbor with a daughter had a favor,
   So I gave her a little kiss like this.

4. See-saw swinger with the boys in the school
   And your feet flyin' up in the air,
   Singin' "Hey diddle, diddle." with your kitty in the middle
   Of the swing like you didn't care.
   So I took a big chance at the high school dance
   With a missy who was ready to play.
   Was it me she was foolin', cause she knew what she was doin'
   When she told me how to walk this way.

Wanted Dead Or Alive

Words and Music by Jon Bon Jovi and Richie Sambora

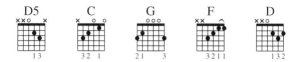

Strum Pattern: 1, 3
Pick Pattern: 2, 4

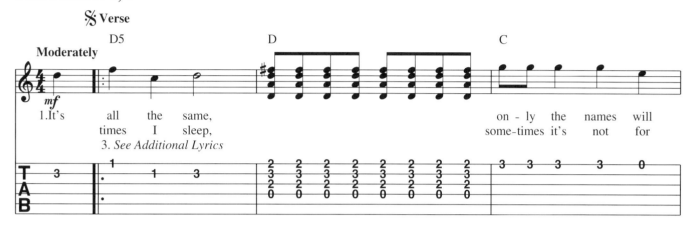

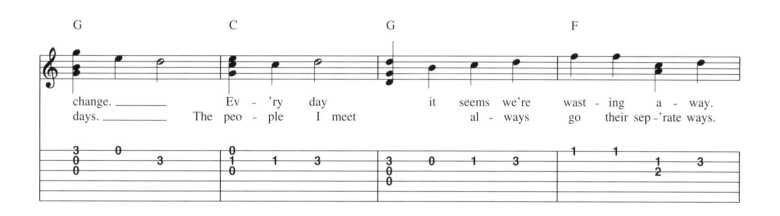

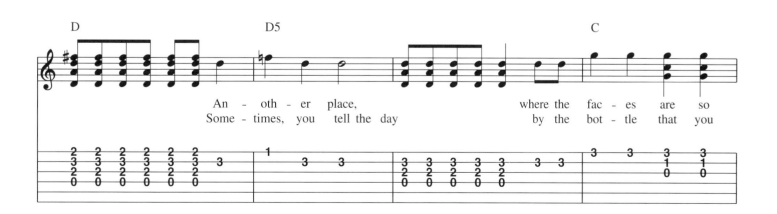

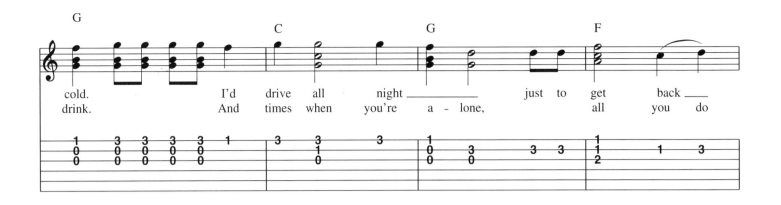

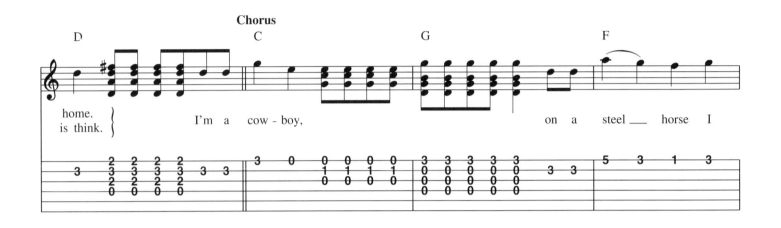

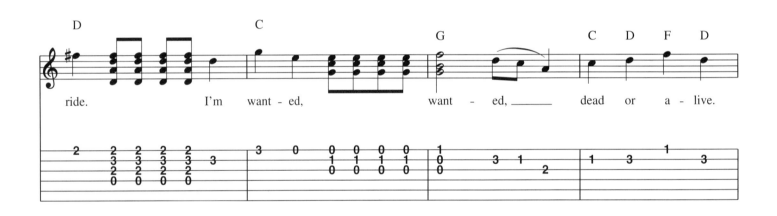

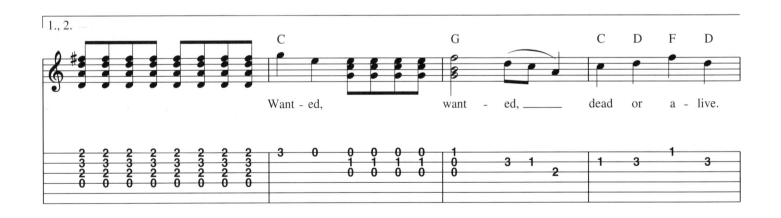

2. Some   'Cause I'm a
3. And I

Outro

cow - boy.   I   got the night on my side. _____ I'm

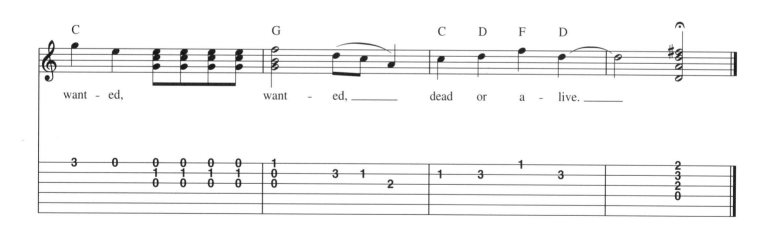

want - ed,   want - ed, _____ dead or a - live. _____

Additional Lyrics

3. And I walk these streets,
   A loaded six string on my back.
   I've seen a million faces, and I've rocked them all.
   I've been ev'rywhere, still I'm standing tall.
   I play for keeps, 'cause I might not make it back.

A Whiter Shade of Pale

Words and Music by Keith Reid and Gary Brooker

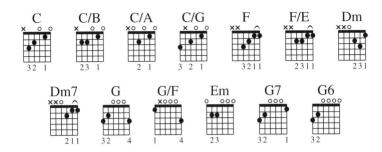

Strum Pattern: 3, 4
Pick Pattern: 3, 5

Intro
Slowly

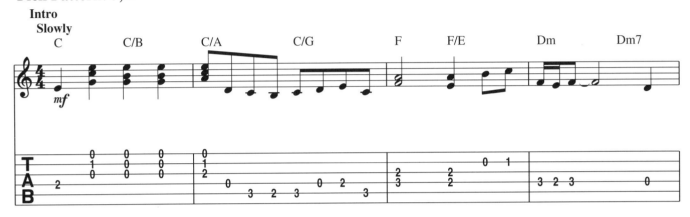

Verse

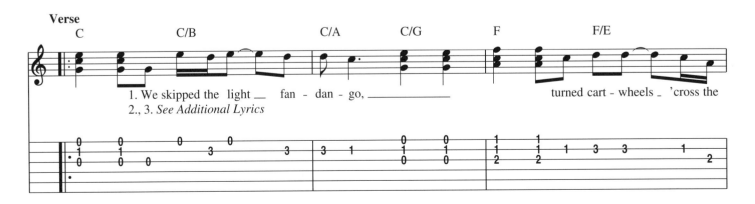

1. We skipped the light __ fan - dan - go, _____ turned cart - wheels _ 'cross the
2., 3. *See Additional Lyrics*

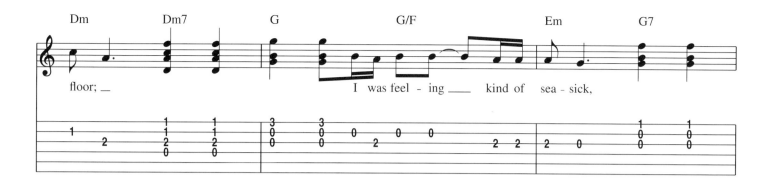

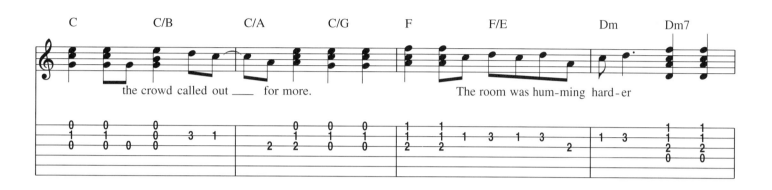

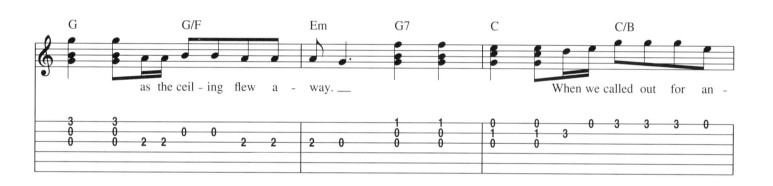

Chorus

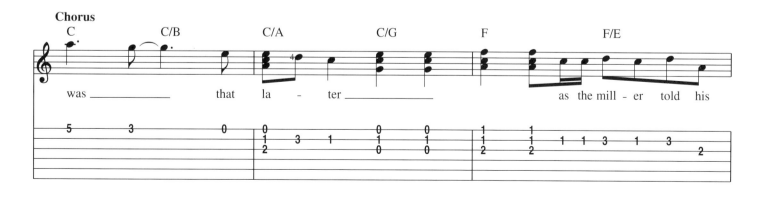

tale, ___ that her face at first just ghost - ly turned a

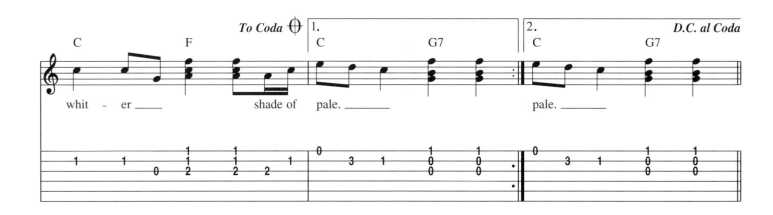

whit - er ___ shade of pale. _____ pale. _____

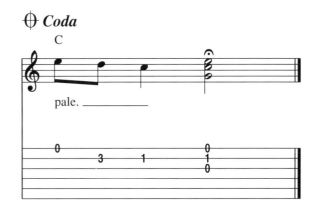

pale. _____

Additional Lyrics

2. She said, "I'm home on shore leave," though in truth we were at sea;
   So I took her by the looking glass and forced her to agree.
   Saying, "You must be the mermaid who took Neptune for a ride."
   But she smiled at me so sadly that my anger straight-away died.

3. She said, "There is no reason, and the truth is plain to see,"
   But I wandered through my playing cards and would not let her be
   One of sixteen vestal virgins who were leaving for the coast.
   And although my eyes were open they might just as well been closed.

Wonderwall

Words and Music by Noel Gallagher

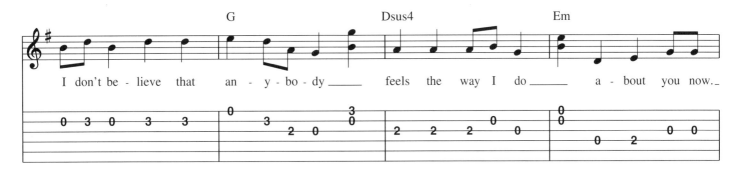

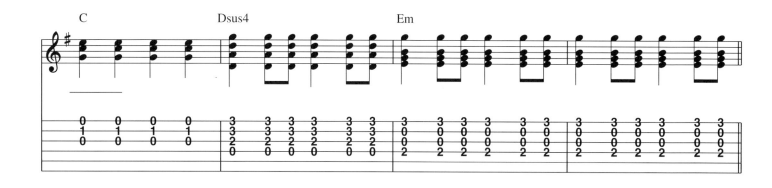

Verse

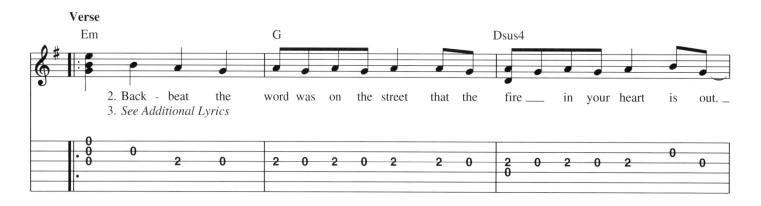

2. Back - beat the word was on the street that the fire ___ in your heart is out.
3. *See Additional Lyrics*

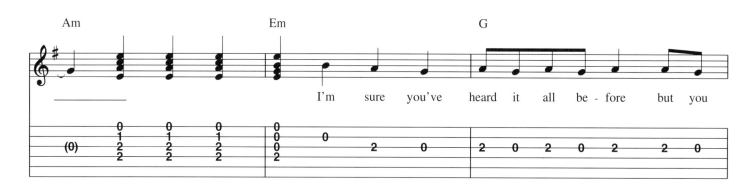

I'm sure you've heard it all be - fore but you

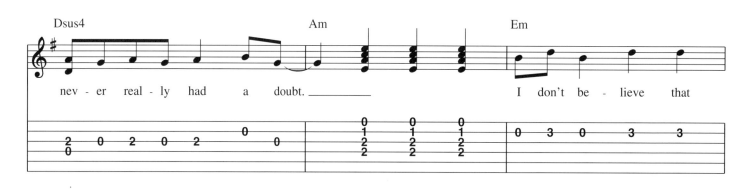

nev - er real - ly had a doubt. ___ I don't be - lieve that

an - y - bo - dy ___ feels the way I do ___ a - bout you now. _

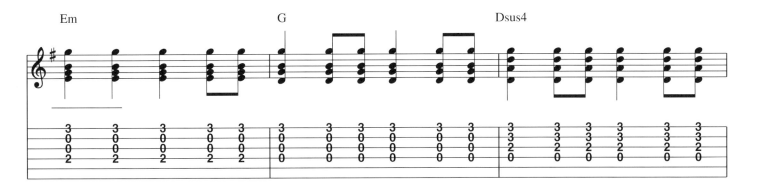

Pre-Chorus

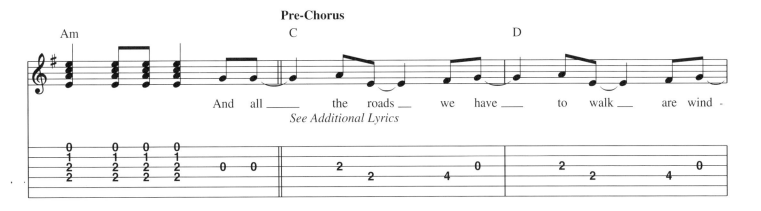

And all _____ the roads ___ we have ___ to walk ___ are wind-
See Additional Lyrics

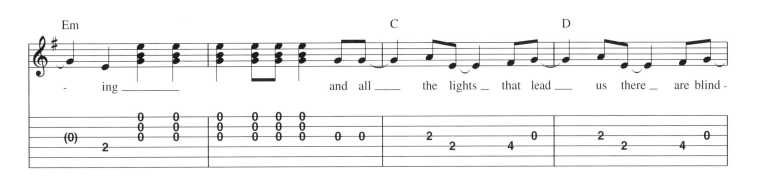

-ing _____ and all ___ the lights __ that lead ___ us there __ are blind-

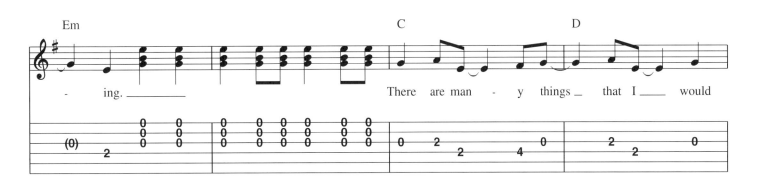

-ing. _____ There are man - y things ___ that I ___ would

like to say to you ___ but I don't know how, _____

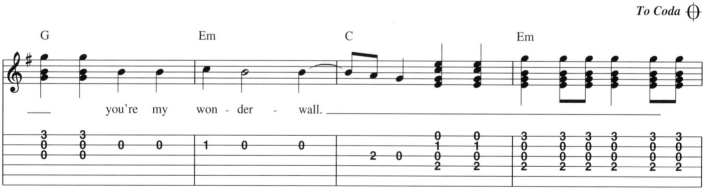

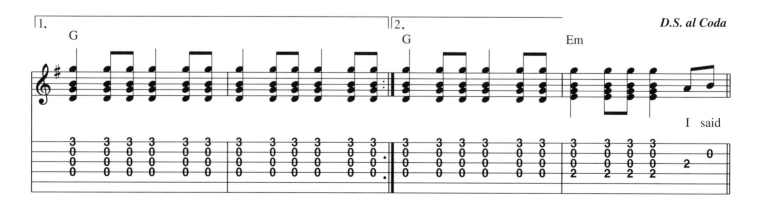

Additional Lyrics

3. Today was gonna be the day
   But they'll never throw it back to you.
   By now you should've somehow
   Realised what you're not to do.
   I don't believe that anybody
   Feels the way I do
   About you now.

Pre-Chorus And all the roads that lead you there were winding
   And all the lights that light the way are blinding.
   There are many things that I would like to say to you
   But I don't know how.

Yellow

Words and Music by Guy Berryman, Jon Buckland, Will Champion and Chris Martin

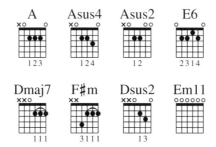

Strum Pattern: 2
Pick Pattern: 4

Intro
Slowly

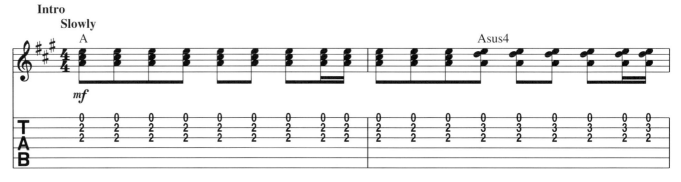

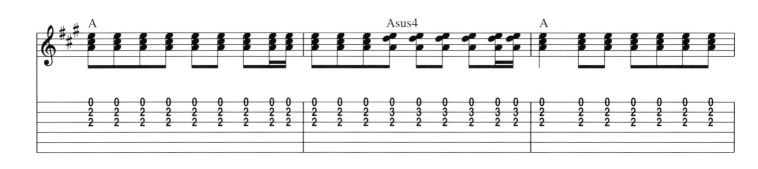

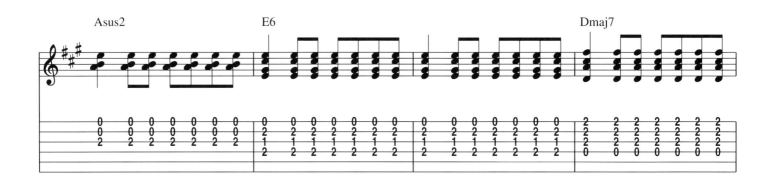

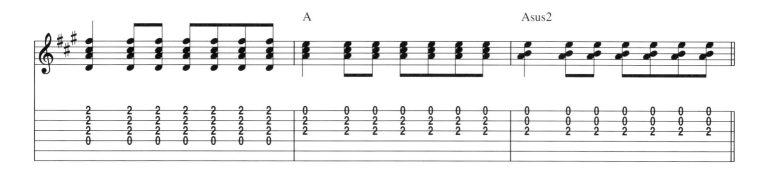

Verse

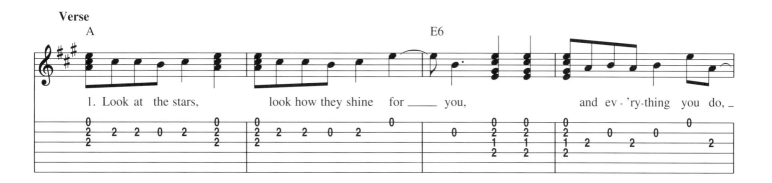

1. Look at the stars, look how they shine for _____ you, and ev - 'ry-thing you do, _

_ yeah, they were all ____ yel - low. _

Verse

2. I came a - long,
3. *See additional lyrics*

I wrote a song for _____ you, and all the things you do, _____

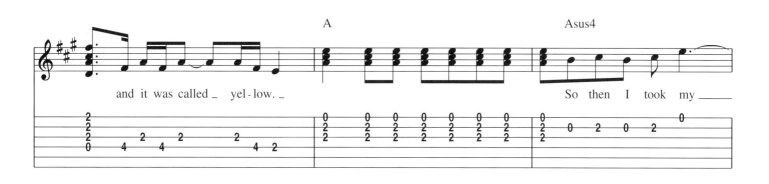

and it was called _ yel - low. _ So then I took my _____

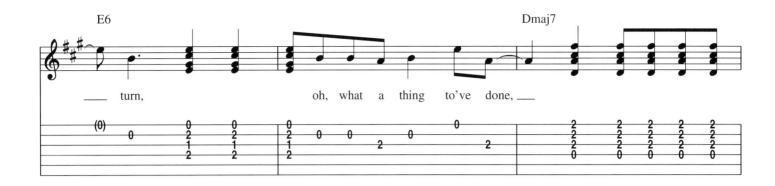

turn,   oh, what a thing to've done, ___

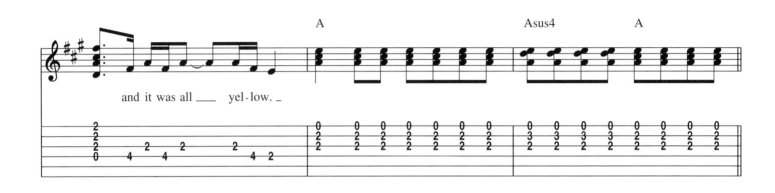

and it was all ___ yel-low. _

Chorus

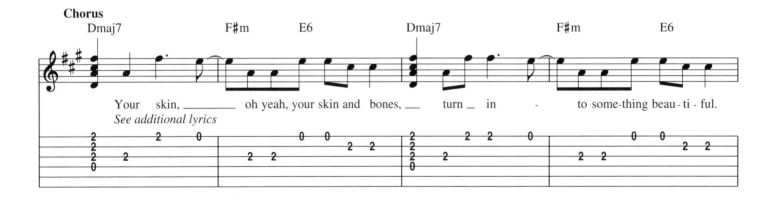

Your skin, _____ oh yeah, your skin and bones, ___ turn _ in - to some-thing beau-ti-ful.
See additional lyrics

And you _ know, _____ you know I love you so, _____ you know I love you so.

Interlude

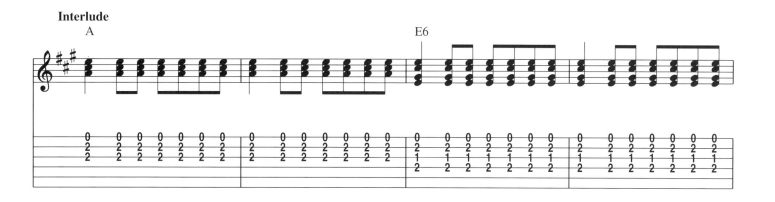

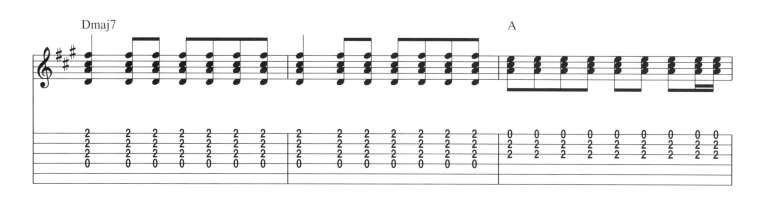

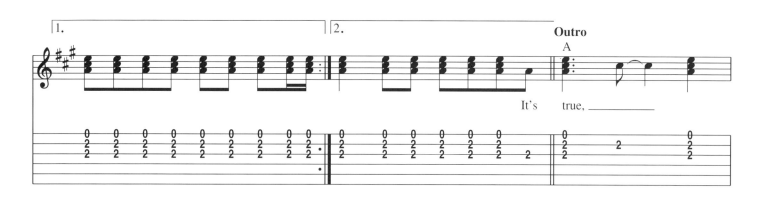

It's true, _____

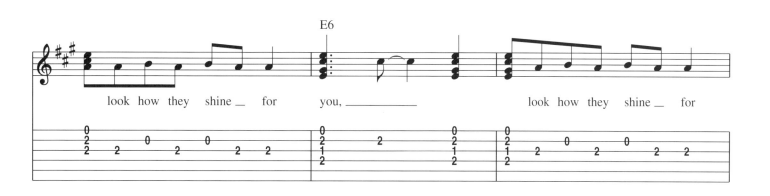

look how they shine _ for you, _____ look how they shine _ for

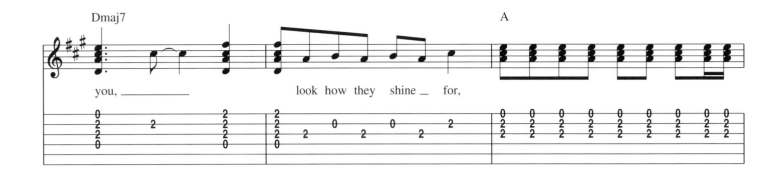

you, _____ look how they shine _ for,

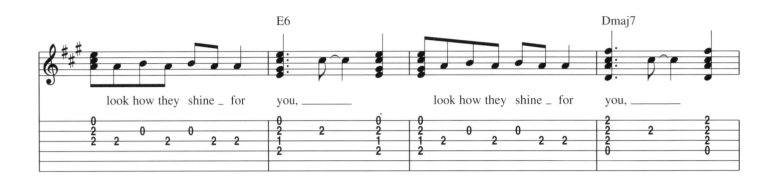

look how they shine _ for you, _____ look how they shine _ for you, _____

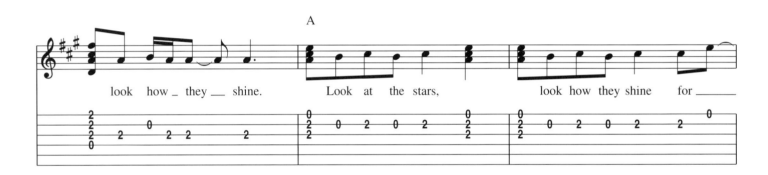

look how _ they _ shine. Look at the stars, look how they shine for _____

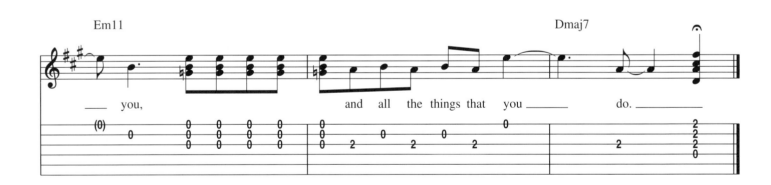

_____ you, and all the things that you _____ do. _____

Additional Lyrics

3. I swam across, I jumped for you,
Oh, what a thing to do,
'Cause you were all yellow. I drew a line.
I drew a line for you,
Oh, what a thing to do,
And it was all yellow.

Chorus Your skin, oh yeah, your skin and bones,
Turn into something beautiful.
And you know, for you I'd bleed myself dry,
For you I'd bleed myself dry.

You Give Love a Bad Name

Words and Music by Jon Bon Jovi, Richie Sambora and Desmond Child

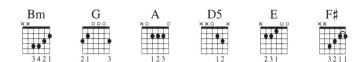

Strum Pattern: 4
Pick Pattern: 3

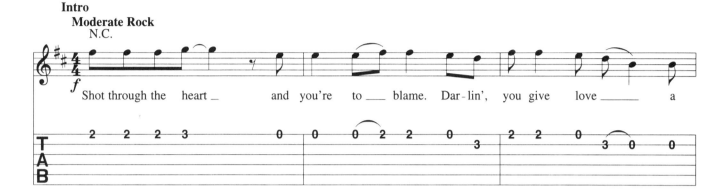

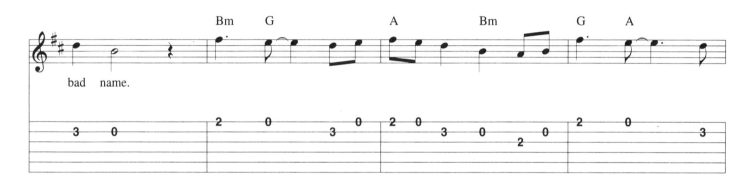

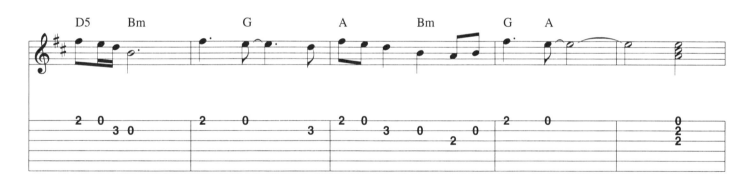

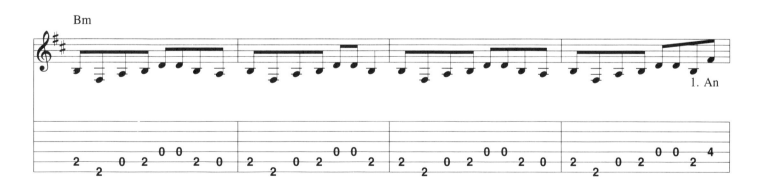

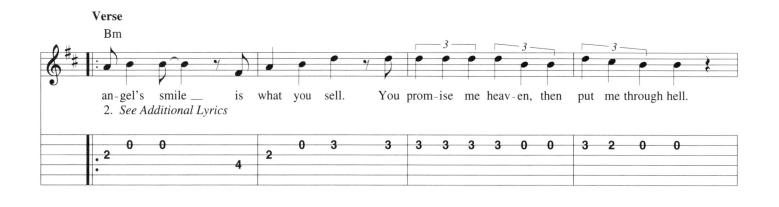

Verse

an-gel's smile __ is what you sell. You prom-ise me heav-en, then put me through hell.
2. *See Additional Lyrics*

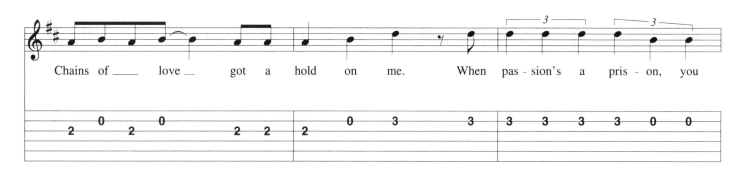

Chains of ___ love __ got a hold on me. When pas-sion's a pris - on, you

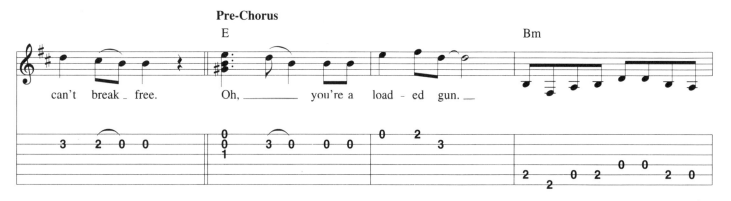

Pre-Chorus

can't break __ free. Oh, _____ you're a load - ed gun. __

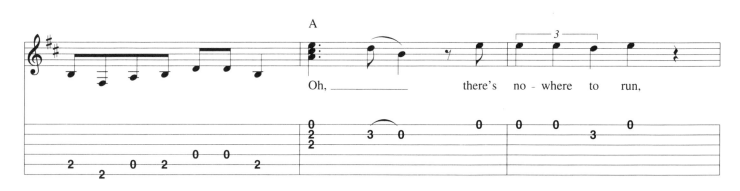

Oh, _____ there's no - where to run,

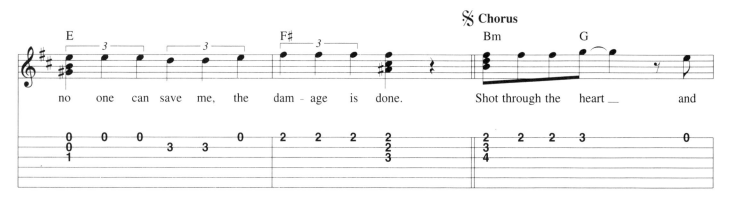

Chorus

no one can save me, the dam - age is done. Shot through the heart __ and

Additional Lyrics

2. You paint your smile on your lips.
   Blood-red nails on your fingertips.
   A schoolboy's dream, you act so shy.
   Your very first kiss was your first kiss goodbye.

Yesterday

Words and Music by John Lennon and Paul McCartney

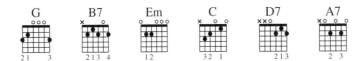

Strum Pattern: 2, 3
Pick Pattern: 2, 4

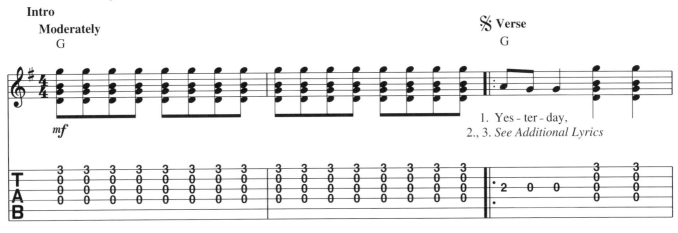

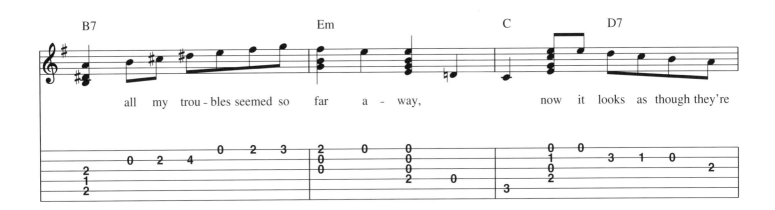

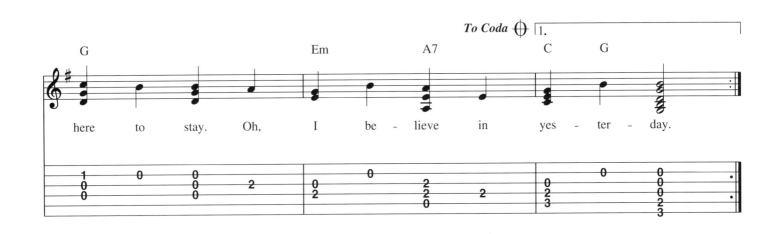

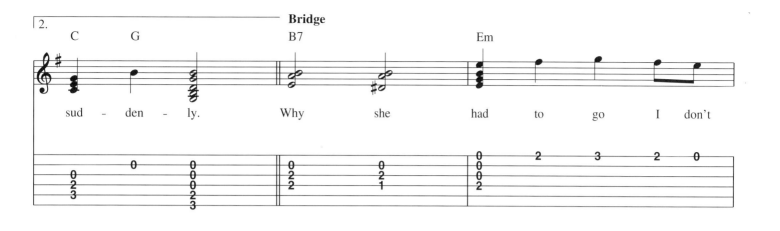

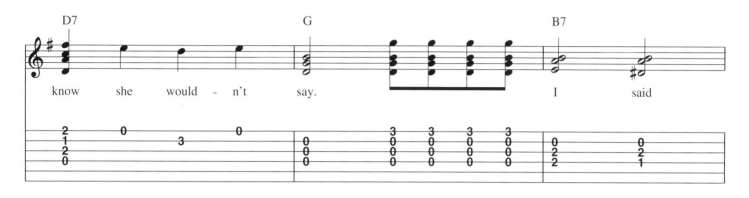

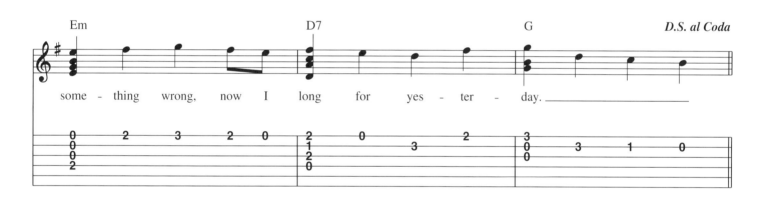

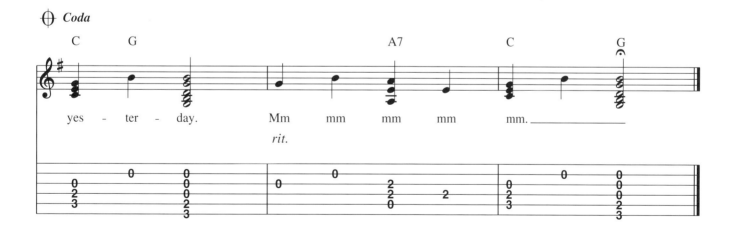

Additional Lyrics

2. Suddenly, I'm not half the man I used to be.
There's a shadow hanging over me. Oh, yesterday came suddenly.

3. Yesterday, love was such an easy game to play.
Now, I need a place to hide away. Oh, I believe in yesterday.

You're Still the One

Words and Music by Shania Twain and R.J. Lange

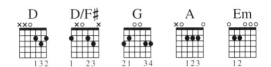

Strum Pattern: 3, 4
Pick Pattern: 4, 5

Intro
Moderately

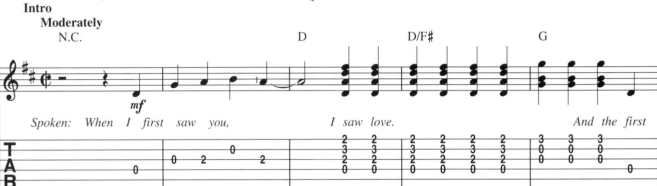

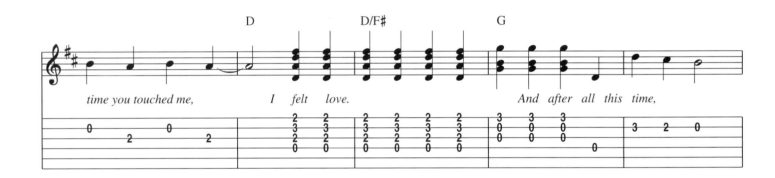

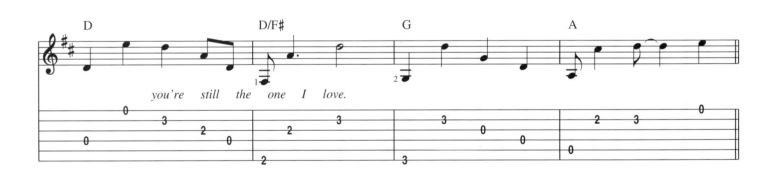

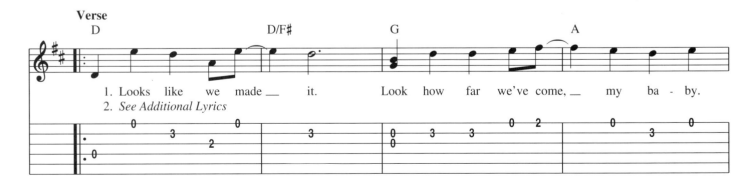

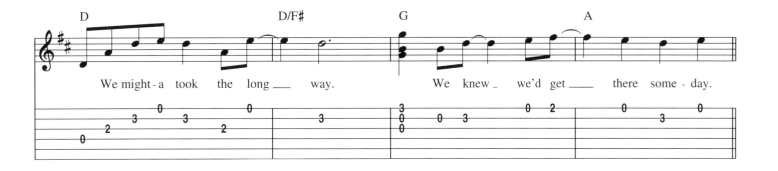

We might-a took the long ____ way. We knew ____ we'd get ____ there some - day.

Pre-chorus

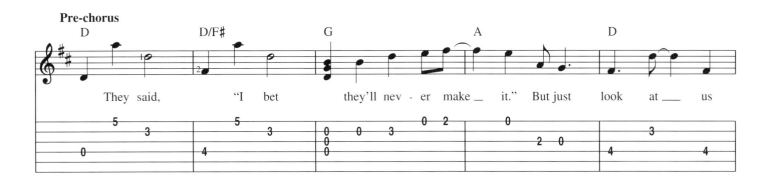

They said, "I bet they'll nev - er make ____ it." But just look at ____ us

hold - ing ____ on. ____ We're still to - geth - er, still go - ing ____ strong. ____

𝄋 **Chorus**

(You're still the one. ____) You're still the one I run to, ____

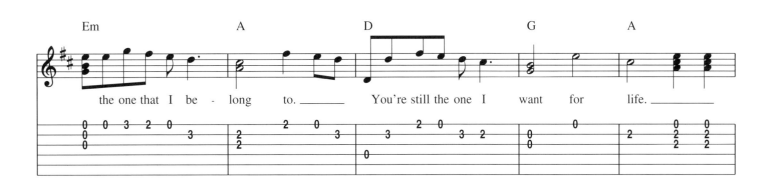

the one that I be - long to. _____ You're still the one I want for life. _____

(You're still the one. __) You're still the one that I love, __ the on - ly one I

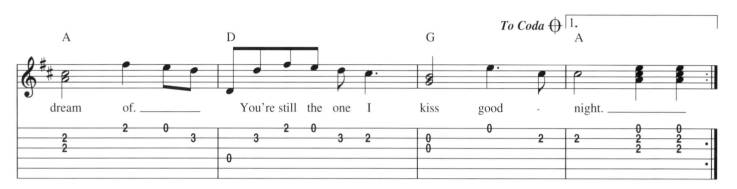

To Coda ⊕ | 1.

dream of. _____ You're still the one I kiss good - night. _____

2. | night. _____ You're still the one.

Interlude

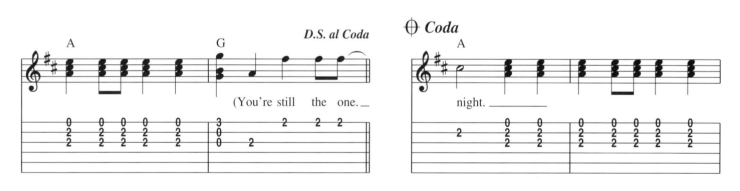

D.S. al Coda

(You're still the one. __

⊕ *Coda*

night. _____

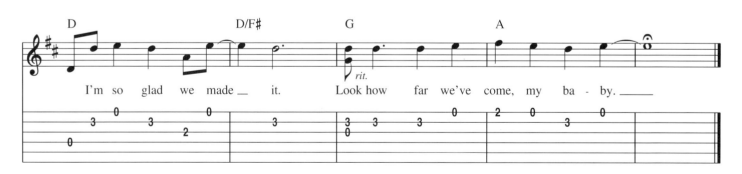

rit.

I'm so glad we made __ it. Look how far we've come, my ba - by. _____

Additional Lyrics

2. Ain't nothin' better,
   We beat the odds together.
   I'm glad we didn't listen.
   Look at what we would be missin'.

Your Song

Words and Music by Elton John and Bernie Taupin

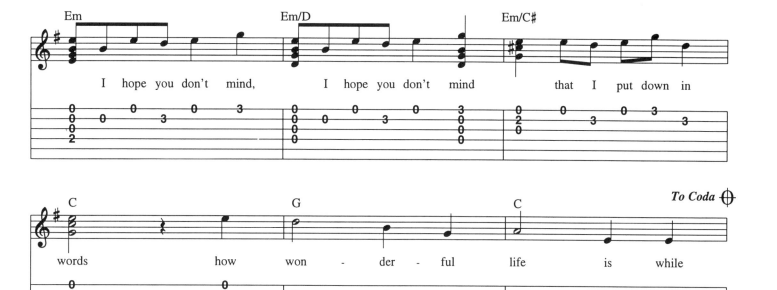

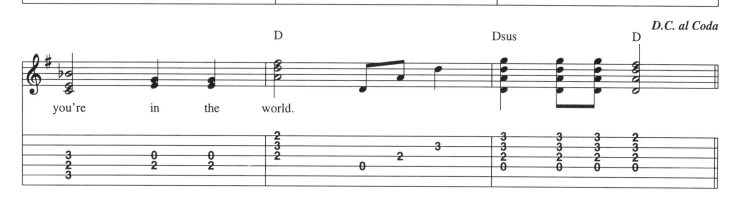

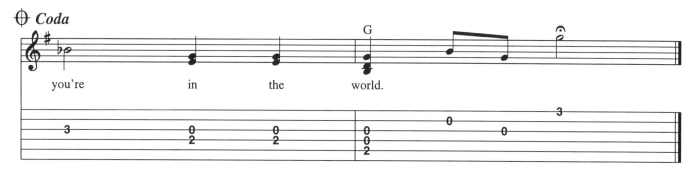

Additonal Lyrics

2. If I was a sculptor, but then again no,
   Or a man who makes potions in a travelin' show.
   I know it's not much, but it's the best I can do.
   My gift is my song and this one's for you.

3. I sat on the roof and kicked off the moss.
   Well a few of the verses, well they've got me quite cross.
   But the sun's been quite kind while I wrote this song.
   It's for people like you that keep it turned on.

4. So excuse me forgetting, but these days I do.
   You see I've forgotten if they're green or they're blue.
   Anyway, the thing is, what I really mean,
   Yours are the sweetest eyes I've ever seen.

Your Cheatin' Heart

Words and Music by Hank Williams

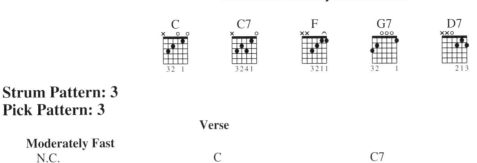

Strum Pattern: 3
Pick Pattern: 3

Verse

Moderately Fast

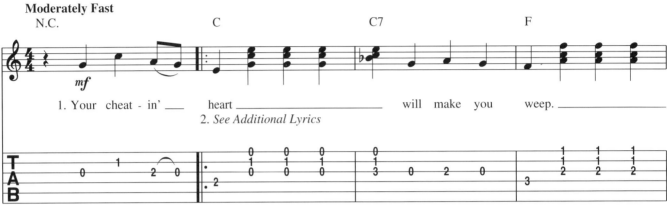

1. Your cheat-in' ___ heart _____ will make you weep. _____
2. *See Additional Lyrics*

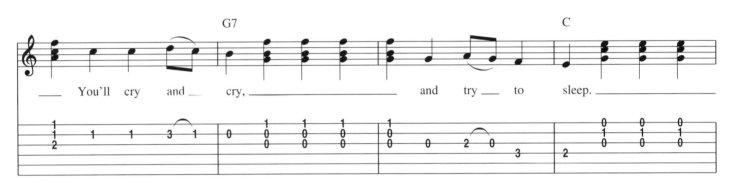

___ You'll cry and ___ cry, _____ and try ___ to sleep. ___

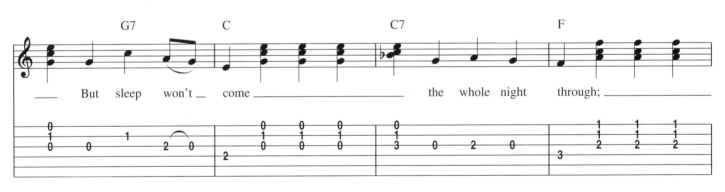

___ But sleep won't ___ come ___ the whole night through; ___

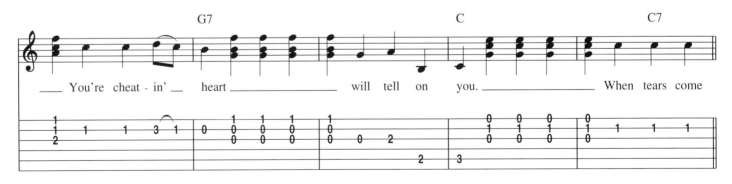

___ You're cheat-in' ___ heart _____ will tell on you. ___ When tears come

Bridge

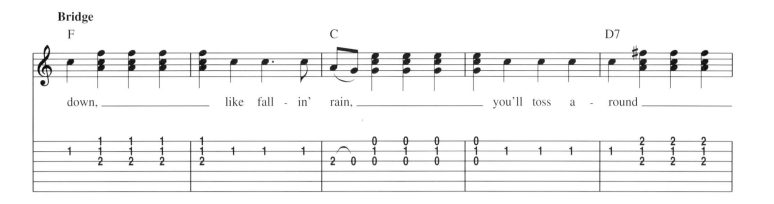

Outro

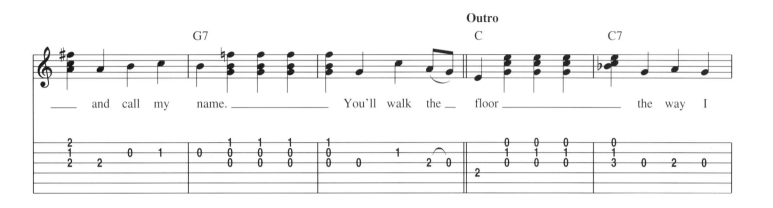

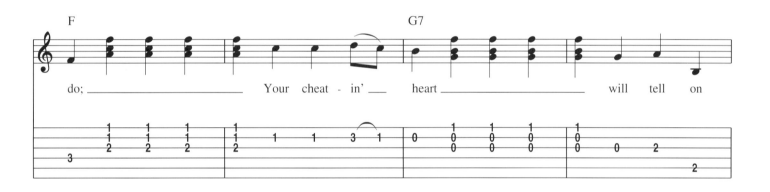

Additional Lyrics

2. Your cheatin' heart will pine someday,
And crave the love you threw away.
The time will come when you'll be blue;
Your cheatin' heart will tell on you.